Transforming Health in London

King's Fund London Commission

Published by
King's Fund Publishing
11–13 Cavendish Square
London W1M 0AN

ISBN 1 85717 169 1

A CIP catalogue record for this book is available from the British Library

Distributed by Grantham Book Services Limited
Isaac Newton Way
Alma Park Industrial Estate
GRANTHAM
Lincolnshire
NG31 9SD

Tel: 01476 541 080
Fax: 01476 541 061

Printed and bound in Great Britain by Biddles Ltd, Guildford and King's Lynn

Cover photograph: Richard Bailey

Transforming Health in London

Contents

Figures

Tables

Boxes

Chairman's preface

The King's Fund was founded one hundred years ago to support health and health care in London. It is fitting, therefore, that in its centenary year the Fund should publish a report designed to improve the health care available to Londoners, and to sustain the capital as an international centre of excellence for health care, medical teaching and research. The report's recommendations have the unanimous support of members of the King's Fund London Commission, which I have had the honour of chairing over the last two years. The Commission's terms of reference and membership are given in Appendices 1 and 2. *Transforming Health in London* rests on a considerable programme of research which is listed in Appendix 3. I am very grateful to everyone who has contributed to it.

Throughout our work, we have taken soundings from a wide range of people involved in health and health care in London. These have included senior London clinicians, chairs of London health authorities, deans of London medical schools, voluntary sector representatives, senior NHS managers and directors of social services from within the capital. I am very grateful to everyone who has given us the benefit of their views.

Lastly, thanks are due to the King's Fund London Commission Secretariat. Nicola Delaney smoothed our path in innumerable ways with her efficiency, diplomacy and sense of humour. Richard Hamblin was responsible for high-quality data analysis, often under considerable pressure. Special thanks go to Virginia Beardshaw and Seán Boyle who collaborated so productively on the programme overall.

Very many people have contributed to this report by the King's Fund London Commission. All of us will be very happy if in any way we have improved the standard of care of those Londoners in need, whether in hospitals or in primary care.

Summary

The National Health Service in London faces profound challenges. Currently, services are under intense strain. Access to appropriate care for Londoners is jeopardised, and public confidence has declined. In inner London, in particular, there are high levels of deprivation and growing health inequalities. While some of the country's leading hospitals are based in central London, general practice is patchy, 'intermediate' care remains underdeveloped and there is a crisis in mental health services. In 1993 the Government set out to change health services in London. There has been real progress in establishing four main groupings for the future development of specialist medical services, teaching and research. But much remains to be done. Success depends on integrating care to meet individual and community needs. It is necessary now to continue the process of transformation, while safeguarding standards of care in the interim, and re-establishing public confidence. Substantial changes to the organisation and delivery of care are required to achieve this. Critically, this must include the creation of local alliances working within a new policy framework. Future policy must concentrate not only on the Health Service, but also on tackling poverty and unemployment and on the regeneration of the capital.

The health of Londoners

Diversity is London's most distinctive feature, with a striking variety of ethnicity, cultures, poverty and wealth within different parts of the city. Health services in the capital must address extremes of affluence and deprivation and differences of culture and race greater than anywhere else in the UK. London has a much higher proportion of people from minority ethnic groups than any other part of the country. With 12 per cent of the British population, London has 49 per cent of the nation's minority ethnic communities. This proportion is expected to increase over the next 20 years in all age-groups.

The health and life expectancy of Londoners is, if anything, slightly better than that of people living in comparable parts of other English cities. However, as elsewhere, there is a clear link between poverty, ill-health and premature death. Between 1981 and 1991 health inequalities in London increased.

Deprivation and the younger-than-average population contribute to exceptionally high rates of mental illness in the capital. Although there are relatively fewer older people living in London than in other parts of the country, their average age is higher than elsewhere, and disadvantaged groups are disproportionately represented within the capital's older population.

Modernising health services

Forces for change

A number of influences are forcing a fundamental restructuring of health service systems both internationally and within the United Kingdom. People are better informed about and more involved in their health and health care. They expect quick access to high-quality care and to influence the style of services they receive. Population structures are changing. Although the majority of older people remain fit and active, their growing numbers place demands on health and social care systems and create new requirements for continuity of care and its co-ordination.

Technological changes have increased the range of treatments available and allowed marked improvements in efficiency within acute hospitals. Much care that would formerly have taken place in hospital now happens at home, or in GP surgeries, and there are many more choices to be made between effective treatments. Achieving quality outcomes within tightly constrained resources has become a major imperative for services. New medical workforce and training policies in the United Kingdom are driving change within the hospital service, encouraging sub-specialisation and the creation of larger clinical teams.

Changing London

In 1993 the then Secretary of State for Health announced *Making London Better*, an agenda for managed change to health services and medical education in the capital. Significant investment in primary care, increased efficiency within London's acute hospitals and the amalgamation of London's medical schools and research institutes have been achieved.

However, delivering positive change in London is a particular challenge. This is because of:

- the size and diversity of the city and its people;

- the complexity of its administrative boundaries, with the fragmentation of local government across 32 boroughs and the City of London;

- the parochialism that can result from the very strength of London's institutions;

- the potentially destructive competitiveness that comes from large numbers of similar providers within the city;

- the extent of flows of patients across the capital, which dilutes the influence of individual health authorities;

- the likelihood of conflicts being magnified by proximity to Westminster and the national media.

Strains on London's services

There are clear signs of strain within London's health and social care system. Health authorities face pressing financial problems, and trusts are struggling to meet financial targets. A number of London trusts are being supported through 'transitional relief' from central funding. Although plans to reconfigure acute hospital services have caused enormous controversy, implementation has stalled because of delays in agreeing capital funding for redevelopment under the Private Finance Initiative. This, and opposition from sectional interests, has stymied the rationalisation of acute specialties.

Acute bed numbers have fallen to close to the average for England, but hospital sites have not closed. Overheads are spread over a smaller service base, contributing to the high cost of care in London. Moreover, spreading a smaller number of beds across the same number of hospitals has reduced flexibility to deal with peaks in emergency admissions. This and moves to day surgery, which have reduced the number of beds which can be switched to emergency use when required, contribute to the fact that London's hospitals have coped badly with winter pressures in 1995/96 and 1996/97. These very public failures fuel resistance to change in the capital.

There is failure of co-ordination of care for older people. Shortfalls in funding for community care have meant that London's social services departments find it difficult to fund care packages and residential and nursing home placements. This has delayed discharges from hospital. At the same time, home nursing, rehabilitation, nursing homes and other forms of 'intermediate' care remain a persistent gap in the capital's service system.

The performance of general practice still lags behind that in other parts of England, and equivalent parts of other English cities. Hospitalisation rates for people in inner-deprived London have fallen well below those of comparative areas outside the capital. Older people are particularly affected by this. London's minority ethnic communities find services poorly equipped to meet their needs.

Skill shortages have deepened over the last five years. Problems with recruitment and retention in psychiatry, paediatrics and accident and emergency services are persistent in the capital, and morale within general practice and mental health services is low. Mental health services are under severe strain. There are unacceptable delays in accessing care, admission thresholds are higher than elsewhere and nowhere in the capital is a comprehensive range of psychiatric services on offer for Londoners.

In the medium term, changes to the funding of NHS research and development – upon which many inner London hospitals depend for a significant proportion of their income – could have a destabilising effect on the city's health care system.

Transforming health

This practical and policy log-jam means that it is particularly difficult for London's service system to adapt constructively to forces for change. At the same time, Londoners' ability to access appropriate care may be jeopardised. To achieve positive change requires the establishment of a new policy framework for service development.

A health services development programme for London

Integrating and ensuring continuity of care across the service system represents the fundamental challenge facing the NHS and its local government partners at the turn of the century. This means delivering treatment, care and support correctly calibrated to individual needs. Services such as emergency care need to develop as interlocking networks within which different elements work interdependently to achieve high-quality outcomes for patients. Such care must be developed locally and tap local initiative and enthusiasm: the diversity of needs in London and the complexity of patterns of provision mean that there can be no central blueprint.

A service development programme in six key areas is required.

- **The health of Londoners.** Links must be forged to connect health care for individuals and communities with a strong public health strand within modern urban planning.

- **Primary care.** The NHS (Primary Care) Act 1997 has created new opportunities for developing primary care as a coherent service. These require careful management by health authorities if London is to equal progress made in other parts of the country.

- **Rationalising London's hospital services.** Networks which link primary, secondary and tertiary services must replace the current piecemeal arrangements. University-based medical education and research centres need to collaborate effectively with health authorities and trusts to ensure a sound basis for medical education and world class research.

- **Intermediate care.** Rehabilitation, intensive home nursing, nursing homes and other 'intermediate' services need to be developed across organisational boundaries in collaboration with local government, to ensure that Londoners retain local access to care.

- **Mental health.** A sustained programme of service development is required with special emphasis on aligning the contributions of health and local government. Meeting the needs of London's deprived communities requires increased resources.

- **Older people.** The capital's health commissioners need to join with local government and with older Londoners themselves to plan more comprehensively for older citizens' well-being. This should concentrate on supporting older Londoners to remain fit, well and self-sustaining and on securing continuity of care across the service system if they become ill or disabled. Age should not be a barrier to accessing care.

The political culture of the NHS must be fundamentally recast to achieve this across London. This process must resolve the inherent tension between 'top down' methods based on central control and 'bottom up' approaches based on local initiative. This means negotiating a middle way, to combine the best features of both.

This requires:

- a central role for government in defining key parameters – notably finance – and setting policy directions;

- enhanced efforts by government to ensure the consistency of strategic priorities, human resources policies and access to capital;

- policy frameworks, incentive structures and monitoring arrangements which reward joint action by local agencies – in particular the NHS and local government;

- new emphasis on – and investment in – health authorities' service design and development capacities.

Success depends on moving away from both 'market' mechanisms and traditional 'command-and-control' systems to structures based on negotiation within clear policy frameworks. Health authorities, trusts and primary care agencies must collaborate effectively with other interests to develop co-ordinated service systems. This can be achieved within 'local health economies' – that is, collaborative groupings involving the statutory authorities, clinicians, service users and other interested parties within different sectors of London.

Recommendations

The lack of strategic direction, appropriate rules and incentives has stalled progress in London. The political culture within which health services development takes place must change to one of active negotiation between the centre and the collaborative coalitions the King's Fund London Commission has termed 'local health economies'. These would be responsible for negotiating local strategies for each of the Commission's six key service development areas.

The Commission's recommendations centre on creating the right policy framework to support this service development programme and to mobilise the contributions of local agencies, clinicians and the public. The recommendations cover:

- public health policies;

- a new strategic framework to support health services development in the capital;

- new mechanisms for allocating resources;

- human resources policies which are firmly linked to service development.

1 PUBLIC HEALTH POLICIES

1.1 The Commission recommends the creation of new public health responsibilities for the capital and specific functions for regulating health services provision within the Government Office for London.

These public health responsibilities will include:

1.2 Developing a public health strategy for London, building on community development initiatives which link local government and health services in the renewal of the urban fabric.

1.3 Undertaking a major programme to facilitate public understanding and involvement in the modernisation of health care in the capital.

1.4 Providing a monitoring and information role for health and health care in London.

1.5 Independent assessment and regulation of health services in the capital.

2 A NEW STRATEGIC FRAMEWORK FOR HEALTH SERVICES DEVELOPMENT

2.1 The Commission recommends that local progress is guided within clear development and investment frameworks established and monitored by the NHS Executive.

2.2 The Commission recommends that where local service strategies involve joint commissioning, health authorities and local government are jointly monitored on the progress they have achieved.

2.3 The Commission recommends a clear system of performance-related objectives for health services organisations and individual managers relating to a coherent London-wide change programme, with measurable goals which are consistent across the capital.

2.4 The Commission recommends that health commissioning in London is strengthened by enhancing health authorities' needs assessment and service development and design capacities.

2.5 The Commission recommends that special development agencies be established to support primary care and mental health services development.

3 MECHANISMS FOR ALLOCATING RESOURCES

3.1 The Commission recommends a reassessment of the formula for the allocation of financial resources to health authorities aimed at combining the budget for hospital and community health services with that of family health services.

3.2 The Commission recommends that resource allocation formulae nationally be adjusted to reflect the special intensity of mental health and other health needs in London and other inner cities.

3.3 The Commission recommends the establishment of a review of the relationship between funding streams for health care and social care, with a view to their complete overhaul.

3.4 The Commission recommends that health and local authorities be empowered to pool budgets to secure clearly defined service objectives and development programmes.

3.5 The Commission recommends that an independent agency be created with public service objectives to develop an investment programme for NHS infrastructure in London.

3.6 The Commission recommends that public sector capital funds be made available to ensure the consolidation of the four merged medical education and research centres in London.

3.7 The Commission recommends that London's research and education centres collaborate actively with health authorities to design the networks of organisations and clinicians required to deliver integrated programmes of care.

4 HUMAN RESOURCES POLICIES

4.1 The Commission recommends the establishment of a London-wide review to examine the impact of the 'Calman' changes to medical workforce and training policy.

4.2 The Commission recommends the development of more flexible and, where appropriate, joint training arrangements to facilitate more effective use of skills and improved understanding, co-ordination and teamworking between health and social care staff from different professional backgrounds.

The report of the King's Fund London Commission rests on a comprehensive programme of analysis of health and social services in London. This is available as five research reports to the Commission. These are intended to inform the future development of health policy in London.

The Commission presents its findings and recommendations to the Government, to the Executive of the National Health Service, and to everyone with an interest in health working within and outside health services and local government in London, as well as to Londoners themselves.

Introduction

Health in the city

London is a vast and complex metropolis. One of the most cosmopolitan cities in the world, it has more than 37 nationalities significantly represented among its residents. As the principal gateway for newcomers to the country, it is the most ethnically and culturally diverse part of the United Kingdom. Diversity is a source of the city's energy and magnetism. The variety of London's landscapes, its urban villages and neighbourhoods, its workplaces, races, cultures, languages and ways of living all contribute to the city's dynamism.

Extremes of wealth and poverty exist side by side, with sharp differences of income, experience and expectation between neighbourhoods and even adjacent streets. Districts a short bus ride apart contrast strikingly: the dilapidation and poverty of the East End is heightened by the City of London's imposing wealth.

Health in London

The health of London has its roots in the capital's diversity. The living, working and leisure conditions of the city shape the opportunities and choices available to its citizens at every stage of their lives. Their health is bound up in this. Well-being and illness, disability, disease and life expectancy are influenced by life – and life chances – in the city.

During the 1990s differences of income within the capital have become greater, accentuating differences of opportunity within it. Londoners' health reflects this increasing divide. In the capital, as elsewhere, communities in which income is low, unemployment is high, and housing and environmental standards are poor have worse health than their more affluent neighbours.

Treatment and care from formal health services exist to support individual and community health. Health and health services in the capital should centre on enabling Londoners to, in Katherine Mansfield's words, 'be everything they can be'. The capital's heterogeneity makes this a particularly demanding challenge. Services in London must address extremes of wealth and poverty and diversity of culture and race on a larger scale than anywhere else in the UK.

A system under strain

Four years after the previous government announced *Making London Better*, its programme of change to health services in the capital, it is clear that London's health care is under severe strain. Recognising this, the Secretary of State for Health has announced a review of proposed changes to health services in the capital. It is hoped that the findings and recommendations of the second King's Fund London Commission will prove useful to policy-makers as they seek new directions for the modernisation and renewal of health services in the capital.

Directions for London's health service system

In 1992, the first King's Fund Commission on London set a direction for health and health services in the capital, to be achieved over twenty years. Through it, care would become integrated around individual needs. Primary care would evolve to become the fulcrum of London's health service system. By the year 2010, it would have central responsibility for health promotion, diagnosis and assessment, treatment, referral, care-coordination and the management of long-term conditions across the health and social care system. Primary care practitioners from a variety of professional backgrounds would assist individuals and communities to design and access programmes of care tailored to their needs and preferences.

To establish this system of community-based, patient-centred care, primary care practitioners' own roles need to extend and grow. New linkages with specialist colleagues in community health and hospital services and across the span of local government are required. Through these new networks, practitioners will draw on local rehabilitation, respite and palliative care, and a range of community-based advice and treatment for people with health problems living at home or in other community settings.

Londoners will need to play an active part in shaping the different elements of the new service system and the links between them. As individual patients they will take an increasingly active role in their own treatment and care.

In the twenty-first century, as today, diagnosis, investigations, treatment and care which require the use of expensive equipment and a range of highly-skilled personnel will take place in acute hospitals and day case units. Medical and surgical specialisation and sub-specialisation will increase the need for collaboration between and within specialist and local hospitals. Primary care practitioners will act as guides through a service system where roles, relationships and the respective contributions of specialist and generalist elements are clear, and where real choices about effective treatment can be presented to individuals.

Transforming health care

Configuring health services in this way demands a new concentration on the needs of Londoners and their communities. At the end of the twentieth century we have come to understand more fully that health – rather than health care institutions and structures – is the proper focus of health policy and its implementation. The health of Londoners is shaped by the whole life of the city. As health services for Londoners are modernised to meet the challenges of the new century, this process needs to be firmly linked to the wider economic and social regeneration of the capital as a whole.

Realising this vision requires much more than a simple reconfiguration of services. A transformation is required in which each level and sector of health care relates to the individuals they serve, to each other and to the economic life of the city in a different and more coherent way. Its achievement implies changes to institutions, professional training and practice, and health services funding. New ways of involving individuals and communities in real choices about their own health and health services are fundamental to it.

Principles for implementation

In 1992, the first King's Fund Commission on London articulated four principles to guide the reshaping of health services in London. Five years into the change programme, they remain apposite:

- **London's health services must be planned and managed to serve the city's population rather than to perpetuate institutions.** This means starting from the health care requirements of the city's population, and the need to reduce health inequalities within the capital. Patients from outside the city should be served when the extra costs of treatment in London are justified by its clinical value.

- **Londoners should be much more actively involved in their own health and health care.** Health services should recognise and respect Londoners' autonomy and individuality. They should be designed to help them make informed choices about their health and treatment. Styles of prevention, care and treatment should be geared to patients' preferences and circumstances, and those of their families and communities.

- **Health care must become primary health care led.** Secondary and tertiary care should become resources explicitly organised to enhance the capacity and support the work of primary health care practitioners. The aim here is to encourage much stronger integration and continuity within programmes of care based on individual patients' needs and preferences.

- **Medical education and research in London should maintain its international excellence.**

Purpose of this report

In the light of this vision of a transformed pattern of health services in the next century, this report from the second King's Fund Commission on London takes stock of the changes to health services in London since 1992, and considers their impact on the capital's health services system. The first King's Fund Commission recognised that the far-reaching changes to the pattern of health services, medical education and research it recommended would take some twenty years to evolve. With this in mind, the second Commission seeks to comment on the London changes so far, and to consider where new directions are needed.

It does this in the context of the distinctive health needs of Londoners, and the rich variety of the city's many communities. It is clear that there can never be a single blueprint for London's health care. The complexity of achieving desirable change within the closely interwoven pattern of London's health services, medical education and research also means that one-off 'quick fix' solutions are simply unrealistic.

With both these points in mind, the report makes recommendations to policy-makers at all levels that are intended to help with the next phase of health service development in the capital.

Guide to the report

The first chapter of *Transforming Health in London* examines the health of Londoners, and its relationship to the economic life of the city. Chapter 2 discusses policies for health and social services in London, and developments as a result of the Government's *Making London Better* programme, initiated in 1993. Chapter 3 explores the relationship between developments in London and national and international trends in health care. It discusses patterns of health services activity and resourcing in the capital, and highlights strains within the service system.

Chapters 4 and 5 summarise the King's Fund London Commission's special studies on mental health and older people and include recommendations. Chapter 6 discusses how change is achieved, and recommends a recasting of the political culture of the NHS to foster negotiation and local collaboration. Chapter 7 gives the recommendations of the King's Fund London Commission.

Appendix 1 and Appendix 2 list the members of the Commission and its terms of reference respectively. Appendix 3 provides a list of the programme of research undertaken on behalf of the Commission. Appendix 4 lists the geographic classifications of London used in this report. Appendix 5 provides an account of the outcome of the reviews of specialty services in London. The appendices are followed by a detailed Glossary and Abbreviations.

CHAPTER 1

Health in the city

London's people

London is growing. With more than 7 million residents it is by far the biggest city in Europe, and ranks as one of the largest in the western world. For the first time in post-war years, the capital is beginning to expand. This is happening even in the inner city, where the population has fallen since the turn of the last century.

London has a younger population than the rest of the UK. Its natural growth rate – the sum of births less deaths in the resident population – is the highest in the country. Since the mid-1980s this has tended to exceed the number of people moving out of the city (Office for National Statistics, 1996).

Young people congregate in inner-deprived London. A quarter of the population of East London and the City Health Authority are under 15, and nearly three-quarters are under 45. Outer London's population is relatively older.

The capital, and particularly its inner boroughs, has always acted as a magnet for young people. This applies especially to young women, for whom employment opportunities are better than in the rest of the country. Two trends – the inward migration of young people and outward movements of people at or around retirement age – and the relatively higher proportion of women living in the capital are enduring features of the London scene (Office for National Statistics, 1996).

London is also a centre for people migrating into the UK. In recent years, this has included refugees or asylum-seekers. Studies indicate that 85 per cent of people granted refugee status have settled in London, with the majority living in inner London. An estimated 100,000 people in the capital are refugees or are awaiting a decision on their refugee status (London Research Centre, 1996).

Figure 1.1 shows projected percentage changes in London's population between 1991 and 2011 by type of socio-economic area. The proportion of people below retirement age is expected to continue to rise, while the number of people aged over 65 is expected to drop overall. Within this, the number of people aged 85 and over is projected to rise by some 14 per cent in the period to 1996. The pattern in London contrasts with the expected trends for the rest of England and Wales, where a steady increase in people aged 75 and over is projected over the next ten years, as Figure 1.2 shows (Boyle and Hamblin, 1997).

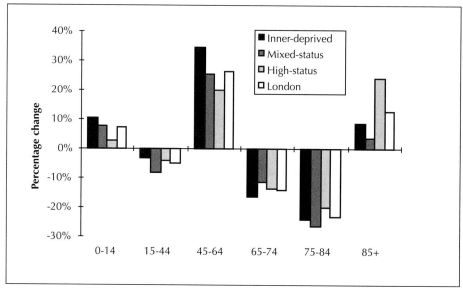

Source: Boyle and Hamblin (1997)

Figure 1.1 Projected percentage changes in population, between 1991 and 2011, by age-group, London

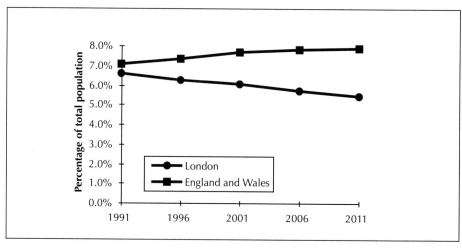

Source: Boyle and Hamblin (1997)

Figure 1.2 Projected change in the proportion of total population aged 75+, between 1991 and 2011, London and England and Wales

London has one of the lowest average household sizes in the UK as a result of its younger age structure. In 1991, people living on their own became the commonest household type in the capital. The structure of the capital's households is quite different from the rest of Britain: London has considerably more households which do not contain a family, more lone-parent families and fewer households with children. Nearly 29 per cent of families with children in London and 39 per cent in inner London are lone-parent families, compared to 21 per cent in Britain as a whole (Office for National Statistics, 1996). This proportion has increased sharply over the last 20 years.

Ethnicity in London

In 1991, London was home to 1.35 million people from minority ethnic communities: 20.2 per cent of the city's population. This proportion is much higher than that of any other region of the country. With 12 per cent of the total population, London has 45 per cent of the minority ethnic population of Great Britain.

There is extreme variation in the distribution of minority ethnic communities across the London boroughs. At 45 per cent, Brent has the largest proportion of people from minority ethnic groups, followed by Newham and Tower Hamlets with 42 and 36 per cent respectively. In contrast, there are seven outer-London boroughs where the white population comprises over 90 per cent of the total, with the highest proportion in Havering, at 97 per cent.

The two largest minority ethnic groups in London are Indians and Black Caribbeans. They tend to live in different parts of the capital, with Indians in outer west London, and Black Caribbeans in Lambeth, Hackney, Brent and Lewisham. London's Pakistani population lives mainly in Waltham Forest and Newham, while 43 per cent of London's Bangladeshi population lives in Tower Hamlets, where it forms almost 23 per cent of the population (Office for National Statistics, 1996).

London's minority ethnic population is expected to increase. Black populations are expected to grow by 52 per cent and Asian populations by 34 per cent in the years to 2011. Figure 1.3 shows the expected changes in ethnic groups in London to 2011.

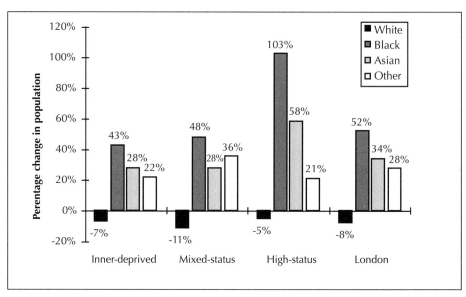

Source: Boyle and Hamblin (1997)

Figure 1.3 Projected percentage changes in population, between 1991 and 2011, by ethnic group, London

London's economy and employment

Like other cities in the developed world, London has experienced a major restructuring of its economy over the last 20 years. Between 1982 and 1994 manufacturing employment in the capital almost halved. Today, more than 80 per cent of the capital's employment is in the financial and service sectors, a much higher proportion than anywhere else in the country.

This de-industrialisation has left scars. Over the past 15 years, London has consistently lost jobs. This has happened both in times of recession and in periods of economic expansion. During the 1980s, the capital lost jobs while the rest of the country gained them. During the deep recession of the early 1990s, the rate of job losses in London was twice the national average. The decline has been greatest in the inner city, and particularly in the traditional manufacturing centres in the East End (Government Statistical Service *et al.*, 1996).

Employment has declined in the capital at the same time as its population has begun to increase. This is especially true in inner London. In the 1990s, London has experienced consistently higher unemployment than the rest of the country – in 1996 the London rate was 3 per cent greater than the UK average and higher than any other part of the country. This has reversed the post-war pattern in which employment rates in London were generally higher than the rest of the country. Londoners from minority ethnic groups are substantially more likely to be unemployed. In inner London, where they make up a quarter of the labour force, they account for 40 per cent of unemployed people (Office for National Statistics, 1996).

Long-term unemployment is particularly serious in London: in 1995, of all people out of work, 42 per cent had been unemployed for over 12 months compared to a national average of 36 per cent. Of the ten English districts with the highest unemployment rates, seven are in inner London. Only 11 boroughs in London have a lower than average unemployment rate, and all of them except for the City of London are in outer London. These high rates of long-term unemployment in the capital reflect a serious skills mismatch between the demands of the city's economy and the skills of its resident workforce (Government Statistical Service *et al.*, 1996).

Income in London

In 1996, the Joseph Rowntree Foundation Inquiry into Income and Wealth reported a rapid growth in income inequality in Britain between the late 1970s and the mid-1990s. Three factors – a growing gap between those with earnings from work and those without earnings; growing numbers of people without earnings; and a widening of income distribution between people in work – contribute to the increasing divide (Joseph Rowntree Foundation, 1995).

Incomes in London reflect this increase in inequality. Moreover, incomes in the capital are more sharply polarised than in the rest of the country. In 1994/95, some 35 per cent of households in the capital had an income per week of £475 or more, compared with 28 per cent in England, while approximately 22 per cent of households in the capital had a gross income below £125 per week, a proportion which is similar to that of the rest of the country. However, the higher cost of living in London – which is some 18 per cent above the rest of England – is likely to mean greater relative deprivation for this group of Londoners. Low pay is disproportionately concentrated among people from minority ethnic groups and on women in the capital.

Over 1.5 million Londoners were dependent on income support in 1994. The number of people who rely on benefit has increased in the 1990s, reflecting London's increased rates of unemployment. In 1989, 15 per cent of inner London residents and 8 per cent of outer-London residents received it. In 1994, the rates were 23 per cent and 13 per cent respectively (London Research Centre, 1996).

Deprivation in London

Deprivation, as measured by the Jarman Underprivileged Area 8 (UPA8) score, is greatest in the eastern parts of London, stretching from the north of Lambeth and Southwark, through Tower Hamlets, Newham and Hackney, to the eastern half of Haringey, as Figure 1.4 shows. The Department of Health's acute and psychiatric needs indices, which measure the need for hospital services, follow a similar geographical pattern to measures of deprivation (see Figure 1.5). Twenty-eight per cent of wards in London have UPA8 scores of over 30 – the level at which GPs in the area attract deprivation payments for their patient lists. In 1991, deprivation was greater in London than in the rest of England, using the UPA8 score as a measure.

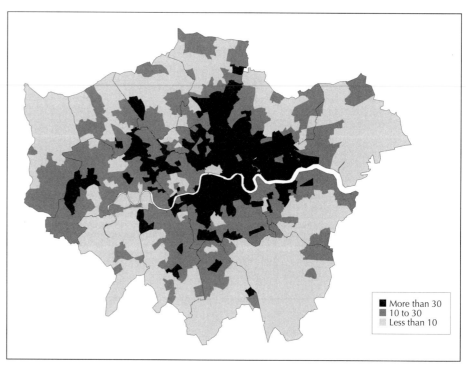

More than 30
10 to 30
Less than 10

Note: Scores greater than 30 attract deprived area payments for GPs

Source: Adapted from Boyle and Hamblin (1997)

Figure 1.4 Underprivileged Area 8 (UPA8) score, by London local authority ward, 1991

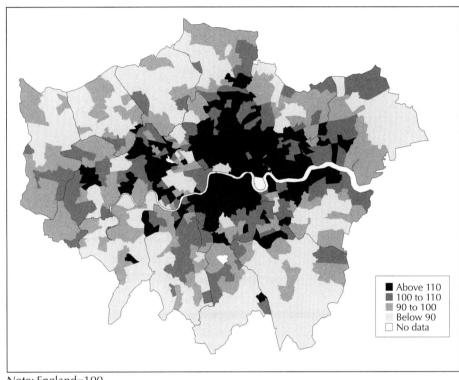

Note: England=100

Source: Boyle and Hamblin (1997)

Figure 1.5 Department of Health acute needs index, by London local authority ward, 1991

Highly deprived wards are not necessarily similar. The most deprived ward in London and in the UK – Spitalfields in Tower Hamlets – has high proportions of minority ethnic populations, unemployment and overcrowding, while the second most deprived – Liddle in Southwark – has very high lone-parent household and unskilled worker scores.

Housing in London

Homelessness is a particular problem in London. Its most obvious manifestation is in the thousands of increasingly young men and women sleeping rough in the capital or in temporary accommodation, bed and breakfasts, squats or hostels. There are an estimated 109,000 single homeless people in London, with an estimated 28,000 in temporary households (London Research Centre, 1996).

Housing quality links directly to health. In many deprived parts of London housing is overcrowded, lacking basic amenities or is damp and cold. Housing costs are high in London, even for social housing. This has important adverse effects on people on low incomes.

The health of Londoners

As in earlier work on the health needs of Londoners conducted for the first King's Fund Commission (Benzeval *et al.*, 1992), an examination of the all-cause, all-age standardised mortality ratio (SMR) shows a ratio for London that is slightly below the England average, at 4 per cent. SMRs range across health authorities in the capital, with an SMR of 87 in Bromley and one of 109 in East London and the City.

Londoners have a broadly similar life expectancy to non-Londoners, with their health being, if anything, slightly better than their counterparts in other English cities. Overall, they have fewer expected years of ill health. This is particularly true of inner-deprived and mixed-status London when compared with similar areas in the rest of the country. The proportion of residents of London DHAs reporting long-term limiting illness ranges from 9 per cent in Kingston and Richmond to 13 per cent in East London and the City, and is closely related to the level of deprivation in the area concerned, as Figure 1.6 shows.

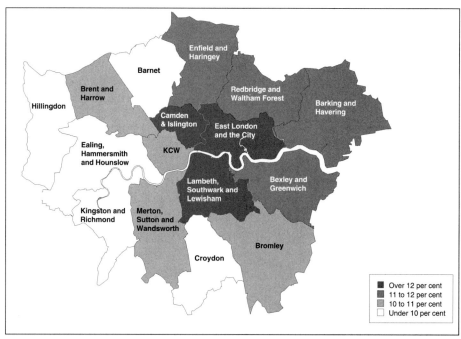

Note: KCW is Kensington, Chelsea and Westminster

Source: Boyle and Hamblin (1997)

Figure 1.6 All-age, long-term limiting illness, London, 1991

The outer London boroughs of Barnet, Bexley, Bromley, Harrow, Richmond and Sutton have relatively low all-age SMRs, and even lower rates for people under 65, indicating levels of population health that are well above the national average. In contrast, inner-London boroughs such as Camden, Hackney, Hammersmith and Fulham, Islington, Lambeth, Newham, Southwark and Tower Hamlets have high all-age SMRs, and even higher ones for people aged under 65 (London Research Centre, 1996). Figure 1.7 shows SMRs for London.

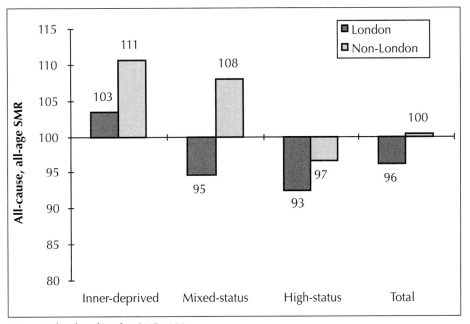

Note: England and Wales SMR=100

Source: Adapted from Boyle and Hamblin (1997)

Figure 1.7 All-cause, all-age SMR, London and England, 1989–1994

However, as Figure 1.8 shows, this relative position changes when SMRs for people aged under 65 are considered. London has an SMR of 104 compared with 99 in the rest of the country. This difference is driven by a high proportion of early deaths in inner-deprived London, which has an SMR of 128. The death rate for men aged between 25 and 55 is particularly high, being 20 to 30 per cent higher than the national figure (London Research Centre, 1996). Mixed-status and high-status parts of London have lower SMRs than their counterparts in the rest of England (Boyle and Hamblin, 1996).

Note: England and Wales SMR=100

Source: Adapted from Boyle and Hamblin (1997)

Figure 1.8 All-cause, 0–64 years SMR, London and England, 1989–1994

Health and deprivation in London

Although on most measures Londoners' health does not compare badly with the health of people in comparable English cities, it demonstrates a clear and predictable link between poverty and deprivation, ill health and premature death. This is particularly true in inner-deprived London, where the effect is very marked, especially for people aged under 65.

Poverty is inextricably bound up with material and social deprivation, which are in turn directly associated with a wide range of indicators of poor health for both adults and children. In London today – as in the rest of Europe – poverty means powerlessness and exclusion from many of the activities and services that the rest of society takes for granted, as well as poor housing and heating and inadequate nutrition. It means restricted opportunities and life chances for poor Londoners and their children. This directly affects their health.

In Britain as a whole, death rates at all ages are two to three times higher among disadvantaged social groups than their more affluent counterparts. People living in disadvantaged circumstances also experience more illness and disability. Most of the main disease groups contribute to these differences, and – as a result – people in disadvantaged circumstances die about eight years earlier than those who are more affluent (Benzeval *et al.*, 1995).

The evidence for this in London is clear from Figures 1.4 and 1.5. A crescent of intense deprivation linked to health need stretches across the east of the city in an arc around the City of London. The maps show how directly material disadvantage is linked to the incidence of disease, disability and earlier death across a range of conditions. The same connections can be seen within the relatively more affluent parts of the city. In districts like Kensington, Chelsea and Westminster, health status is markedly worse in deprived wards, and utilisation rates for health services are also appreciably higher. Pockets of severe deprivation and attendant ill health occur within most high-status London boroughs (Boyle and Hamblin, 1997).

There is nothing surprising or new about these inequalities in health in London. A distinct socio-economic gradient in disease and death rates was first observed in Britain in the 1860s and is evident in countries across the developed world. Over a century of research has shown that low income, poor housing and lower education combine to limit life expectancy and increase illness and disability. These differences exist at all ages (Benzeval *et al.*, 1995).

In Britain, the increases in economic inequality during the 1980s and 1990s is reflected in national data on health status. Between 1981 and 1991, death rates for some of the most disadvantaged groups worsened in relative terms when compared to more affluent areas. In some age groups – for example, for young men – rates actually rose for the first time since the 1930s. London reflects this national picture: between 1981 and 1991 the gradients in mortality ratios between the most and the least deprived wards in the city have increased. The particularly high impact of unemployment on the capital in recent years as well as factors like the high incidence of HIV compared to the rest of the country have contributed to this (London Research Centre, 1996).

Mental health in London

Mental health is a product of genetic, social and environmental factors and the way that these impact upon individuals and families. Unemployment, social and cultural isolation, and the poor living conditions created by poverty all foster vulnerability to mental distress. In inner London these conditions interlock with the capital's high levels of substance abuse, homelessness, and HIV and AIDS to create unusually high levels of mental ill health.

In addition, the capital's younger-than-average population means a greater incidence of psychoses and eating and personality disorders at the stage in which they require the most active intervention by health and social services. Substance misusers are highly concentrated in London: about a third of the people starting contact with drug misuse services in the UK live in the capital. There is also evidence that seriously mentally ill people are attracted to live in inner cities. The high proportion of single-person households in the capital is associated both with higher incidence of illness, and with requirements for greater support to distressed individuals. Epidemiological studies suggest that the incidence of serious mental illness in inner London is twice that of suburban or rural areas.

London's ethnic diversity and the fact that the majority of the UK's refugees live in the capital create particular mental health needs. Both groups experience adversity, with high levels of unemployment and poor housing conditions conspicuous features of their collective experience. Some minority groups experience increased incidence of mental health problems. These factors combine to create the special intensity of mental health needs in deprived parts of London (Johnson *et al.*, 1997).

Older people in London

Older people are under-represented in London's population, particularly in the group aged 65 to 74. The shortfall in this age-group means that the average age of London's older population is higher than in the rest of England. Table 1.1 compares the age structure of London's older population with the rest of England. Overall, the older population of London has been growing less quickly than in other parts of the country, and is now set to fall until around 2011.

Table 1.1 The age structure of London's older population, 1995

Age-group	Older age-groups as percentage of population aged 65+				Ratio of London percentage to rest of England	
	Males		Females		Males	Females
	London	Rest of England	London	Rest of England		
65–69	32.8	33.1	24.7	25.6	0.99	0.96
70–74	28.0	29.0	24.1	25.3	0.96	0.95
75–79	18.5	18.6	19.1	19.1	1.00	1.00
80–84	12.8	12.2	16.6	15.7	1.05	1.06
85+	7.8	7.1	15.5	14.4	1.09	1.08
% of total pop. 65+	11.0	13.4	15.8	18.9	0.82	0.84
Mean age[1]	73.81	73.64	75.86	75.54		

1. An approximation of the average age of the population aged 65+, calculated by assuming that the average of a quinquennial age group is 2 years above the base, e.g. 67 for the 65–69 years age-group.

Source: Adapted from Warnes (1997)

The early 1990s saw a rapid surge in the number of people aged 85 and over. Both estimates and retrospective projections suggest that the number of men in this age group increased by a quarter and the number of women by some 10 per cent between 1991 and 1996. Special factors are responsible for this. There was substantial net migration into London during the 1920s and 1930s, reflecting the capital's relatively buoyant economy during those years. The large proportional increase in the number of men reflects the fact that those aged 85–90 in 1993 were born between 1903 and 1908 and were just too young to fight in the First World War. They were not affected by the death toll of the 1914–18 campaigns and, in comparison to those born five and ten years before, many more have survived into their 80s. This high rate of increase in the oldest age-groups is projected to moderate in the later 1990s, and then to decline between 2006 and 2011 (Warnes, 1997).

Among all British cities and regions, London has the highest rates of out-migration of late middle-aged and older people. For people in their 60s, this exodus tends to be of people from above-average income groups. As a result, the older people who remain include a higher proportion of people from lower socio-economic backgrounds than the capital's working age population.

London has the highest concentration of people from minority ethnic groups in late middle and old age of any part of the country. It will also experience the fastest rate of growth of older people from minority ethnic groups over the next decade. The greatest increases will be among people from Black-Caribbean and Indian ethnic groups. Older people from the Black-Caribbean and Bangladeshi minority ethnic groups tend to live in inner-deprived parts of the capital, while the majority of older Indian-origin people live in outer London. Older people in most minority ethnic groups have low incomes and relatively poor health.

Conclusion

Londoners' health is intimately connected with the economic and social life of the city. The capital displays an age structure and a mosaic of ethnic and cultural diversity that is substantially different from the rest of the UK. Differences within the city are also intense: deprived communities in different parts of the city display markedly different characteristics, and extremes of affluence and poverty exist cheek by jowl. Box 1.1 summarises the distinctive characteristics of Londoners living in different parts of the capital.

The intensity and diversity of needs in the capital pose particular challenges for health services delivery. Nowhere is this more true than for mental health in the inner city, where needs are among the highest in the UK.

In recent years the gap between rich and poor Londoners has widened. As a result, differences in health status have intensified. Increasingly, too, socio-economic gradients in health status now include a racial dimension, as the minority ethnic communities of inner-deprived London grow.

These inequalities clearly relate to the social and economic life of the city, and the opportunities available to Londoners. The growth of long-term unemployment in London during the 1990s and the skills mismatch that exists between the city's service-dominated economy and the inner-city workforce raise the anxiety that inequalities in the health status of Londoners are likely to increase, unless concerted action is taken to improve the life-chances and living conditions available to London's deprived communities.

It is clear from this that the agenda for health in London cannot be pursued in isolation from the rest of life in the city. Nor should it concentrate narrowly on health services. To be effective at addressing the social and economic determinants of ill health it needs to be linked to social and economic regeneration at neighbourhood, borough and city-wide levels.

Box 1.1 Characteristics of London's population

London's population structure differs markedly from the rest of England, with its younger age profile and high levels of ethnicity. Within this, the capital is by no means homogenous. This box examines the distinctive characteristics of the major sectors of the city.

- The north-west sector has a similar age profile to that of London as a whole. Although the level of deprivation in the sector overall is close to the London average, pockets of affluence and extreme deprivation exist side by side, perhaps to a greater degree than anywhere else in the capital. This is particularly noticeable in the boroughs of Kensington and Chelsea and the City of Westminster. A greater than average proportion of the population belongs to Asian ethnic groups, particularly in parts of Ealing, Hammersmith and Hounslow.

- The north-central sector has a similar age and ethnic profile to that of the rest of the capital. There is a noticeable concentration of deprivation towards the south and east of the sector, in Islington and parts of south Camden and east Haringey.

- The east sector has the youngest age profile of anywhere in the capital, with 22 per cent of the population aged under 15 years, compared with 19 per cent in both London and England. Both the greatest concentration of deprivation and the highest absolute levels of deprivation are found in this sector. At 24 per cent, the proportion of the local population belonging to minority ethnic groups is higher than the London average of 20 per cent. Of particular note is the Bangladeshi population of Tower Hamlets, which forms a quarter of that borough's total population, and the Black-Caribbean population of Hackney.

- The south-east sector has a similar age profile to the capital as a whole. There is considerable variation in the levels of deprivation, with high levels of deprivation in Lambeth, Southwark and Lewisham and some parts of Greenwich, and notable affluence in Bromley and parts of Bexley. The population of the south-east sector of London has a larger than average proportion in Black minority ethnic groups and a relatively smaller proportion in Asian groups.

- The south sector's population resembles the rest of the country more than it does the rest of London. Its population is older. There is less deprivation, with no DHA defined as an inner-deprived area. High levels of deprivation are only found in four wards in Wandsworth. A smaller proportion of the population of the south sector belongs to minority ethnic groups than elsewhere in the capital.

An explanation of the five London sectors is given in Appendix 4.

CHAPTER 2

Health services and medical education in London, 1992–97

Introduction

In 1992, the potentially damaging impact on health care in the capital of the implementation of the NHS and Community Care Act 1990 was signalled in two reports: *London Health Care 2010: Changing the future of services in the capital*, the report of the first King's Fund Commission (King's Fund, 1992), and the *Report of the Inquiry into London's Health Services, Medical Education and Research*, which was chaired by Professor Sir Bernard Tomlinson (Tomlinson, 1992).

Both reports stressed the urgent need for investment in London's underdeveloped primary and community health services. Both warned that the capital's hospital services could be undermined by the new internal market. Both saw the consolidation of the capital's acute and specialty services and the establishment of fewer, stronger centres for medical education and research as essential to the delivery of high quality health services to Londoners and to sustaining excellence in the capital's medical education and research.

The need for change in London's hospital services has been recognised for more than a hundred years. *London Health Care 2010* and the Tomlinson report were added to a series of reports and recommendations on London health care and medical education that stretch back to 1892. In 1992, however, change seemed to be at hand. Competition within the new NHS internal market threatened to destabilise London's hospitals, and this threat required a policy response from the Government and action within the NHS.

This chapter discusses this response and the process of implementing change in London, which took place within the complex policy environment created by the 1990 Act. It assesses strengths and weaknesses of attempts to bring about changes to health services, medical education and research in London, and the impact that this has had on the service system. It does so recognising both the great complexity and political risk attached to changing health services within the capital and the fact that the changes begun in the early 1990s would take at least 20 years to work through.

Conflict without change: 100 years of the 'London problem'

Well before the foundation of the NHS, the deep-seated nature of the problems facing London's hospitals was recognised by policy-makers and health care professionals. From the end of the 19th century, the mismatch between London's growing suburban population and the concentration of its hospitals in the centre of the city was apparent.

Later, the isolation of many London medical schools – closely associated as they were with individual London teaching hospitals – and their poor linkages with university-based biological and social science became the subject of policy attention, with repeated recommendations for reform.

Since 1892, a series of 20 reports have chronicled the problems of London's health services and medical education (King's Fund, 1992). Issues they have reiterated include:

- the concentration of acute hospitals, medical schools, research centres and postgraduate institutes in central London, all of which contribute to an expensive pattern of care for a declining inner-city population and inadequate primary, community and continuing care in the capital;
- poor linkages between London's medical schools and the rest of the University of London;
- fragmented and inadequately supported specialist and clinical research units;
- ageing buildings and equipment, with a lack of capital for new developments;
- a management and planning structure that failed to counteract the entrenched parochialism of London's health care providers and to provide direction for the capital's health services overall.

Over more than a century, a series of proposals have been made and restated in report after report. These include the need to amalgamate medical schools and move them and their associated teaching hospitals out of central London; to merge teaching hospitals; to strengthen primary care; to consolidate specialty and research activity; and to improve links with the University of London.

Some change did take place. Between 1906 and 1982, King's, Charing Cross, the Royal Free and St George's with their associated medical schools did move from central London to the inner ring of London suburbs. However, the problems of the capital's poor primary and continuing care remained unaddressed. The bulk of the capital's mental health services remained located in asylums on its periphery until the 1970s and 1980s. Fragmentation of specialty provision, medical education and research persisted. Hospital services continued to be heavily concentrated in the inner city, with underprovision in outer London.

The 'London problem' in the 1990s

In 1989, the Government published *Working for Patients*, the White Paper which set out its intention to establish an 'internal market' within the NHS (Secretary of State for Health, 1989). Health authorities and GP fundholders were to become purchasers of care, with NHS hospital, community and ambulance services to be constituted as 'provider' NHS trusts.

These changes – which were enacted through the NHS and Community Care Act 1990 – held real dangers for London's impacted hospital system. Costs in the capital's teaching hospitals were very high and they relied on flows of patients from outer London and elsewhere in the UK to sustain a concentration of general acute and specialist services within central London. The introduction of the market posed the risk of attrition, since it seemed clear that more distant purchasers would turn to local providers for less costly care. This would undermine the viability of teaching hospitals and other London providers. This threat was the more potent because London health authorities were set to lose resources under the NHS capitation funding formula, with the likelihood that revenue funding for health services in the capital would remain extremely tight to the end of the century.

Conscious of these difficulties, in 1990 the King's Fund established its first Commission on London, with a remit to take a strategic, 20-year view of desirable directions for health services in London. The Secretary of State for Health established his own inquiry into health services, medical education and research in the capital in the autumn of 1991 to examine the immediate impact of the reforms on London.

The King's Fund Commission reported in June 1992, and the Tomlinson report was published in the following October. Details of the recommendations of each report are given in Boxes 2.1 and 2.2 respectively. Both recommended fundamental changes to health services, medical education and research. These involved redressing the balance between primary and secondary care in the capital through a major programme of investment and development in primary and community services, and a concentration of specialties and general acute services on fewer, better-equipped sites. Both considered that consolidation and closure of sites would be accompanied by increases in efficiency and a reduction in acute bed numbers that would bring London in line with the national position. The King's Fund report stressed that consolidation of acute hospitals needed to go in tandem with the development of health centres and rehabilitation and other 'intermediate care' services to preserve local access to care. Acute services rationalisation would be linked to mergers of undergraduate and postgraduate medical schools, with four multi-faculty science centres within the University of London to create a greatly strengthened base for medical education and research.

The King's Fund report envisaged that the changes would lead to a reduction of some 5,000 acute hospital beds across the capital by 2010, and the closure of some 15 acute hospitals over the same period. Tomlinson saw a reduction of 2,000–7,000 beds by the year 2000. Both warned that unless whole sites closed, fixed costs would not be released in the manner required to transfer revenue to fund primary and community developments and capital monies needed for the wholesale modernisation of London's capital stock. This last was of major importance. The NHS in London had a greater complement of ageing Victorian and early 20th century buildings than anywhere else in the country. These were inefficient and increasingly unsuitable places for patient care. Major investment was required to address this (Meara, 1992).

The policy response

Making London Better, the Government's response to the Tomlinson report, was published in February 1993 (Department of Health, 1993a). This set the official strategy for the NHS in London.

Making London Better accepted the case made by Tomlinson for a programme of managed change in the capital, although certain of the report's detailed recommendations were ruled out. It set out four principles for the Government's strategy for improving health and health care:

- people living and working in London must have ready access to the full range of health services that they need;
- services must be of a good standard and cost-effective;
- the internal market for health care should work in London, as elsewhere;
- high quality medical education and research must be sustained and fostered.

The London Implementation Group (LIG) was established to broker major change in the capital's health services and medical education and research in collaboration with the Thames regions, trusts, health authorities, the University of London, the Higher Education Funding Council for England, and the Department of Health. LIG had no statutory authority and its executive powers were very limited, but its chairman sat on the NHS policy board and had direct access to ministers, who were intimately involved in the detail of its early decisions (Nichols, 1997).

Box 2.1: *London Health Care 2010*

London Health Care 2010: Changing the future of services in the capital, the report of the first King's Fund Commission in June 1992, was the first report in a 100-year series on London's health care to examine the options for health services and medical education and research together, and link them with a strategic view of future directions for health care.

The report made the case for substantial modernisation of health services in London. It saw the renewal of London's health services as one part of a wider programme of regeneration for the capital city as a whole. Major investments in primary and community services and the rationalisation of the capital's hospitals and clinical specialties were recommended. The report saw stronger connections between the capital's scattered medical specialties, medical schools and postgraduate institutes and the multi-faculty colleges of the University of London as essential to maintaining London as a world centre of medical education and research in the 21st century.

London Health Care 2010 stressed that the status quo was not an option because the implementation of the NHS and Community Care Act 1990 would subject the capital's health services to pressures that would prove unsustainable. In particular, the introduction of the NHS 'internal market' was likely to result in reductions in traditional flows of patients into inner London because of the markedly higher cost of care in the capital, especially for routine treatments. The clear risk was attrition, in which basic health care for Londoners would be jeopardised along with excellence in medical education and research. In any case, London's hospital estate had a high proportion of outmoded buildings: urgent action to modernise for the next century was required. Substantial capital was required for this, which would need to come from consolidation of sites and land sales.

The report stated that an overconcentration on specialist and elective hospital care meant that Londoners already received a poor deal from the capital's health services, even though more money was spent on them. Primary and community services were markedly worse than those in other English cities, and frail older people and people with mental health problems were particularly disadvantaged by London's historic underinvestment in continuing care and rehabilitation.

The Commission's report stated that 'sustained political will to back major structural change to health care delivery in London' was required if health services for Londoners were to be modernised and the capital's position as a centre of excellence for research and medical education secured for the next century. It said that the involvement and commitment of Londoners and those working in the capital's health services would be essential if a change strategy was to be acceptable.

cont.

London Health Care 2010 recommended three closely interwoven strands of development for health services in London.

- A primary and community health care development programme, to include major preferential investment in service development, information technology and equipment, education and training. Developments should be informed by local needs assessment. Development plans in different parts of London should be agreed and implemented. Investment and service development should be evaluated.

- Reshaping and modernising London's acute hospitals to create an interdependent network of local community-based health care centres, acute general hospitals and tertiary referral centres by:
  - rationalising specialties;
  - consolidating hospital sites to increase clinical and cost effectiveness.

This would permit the capital and revenue savings required for re-investment in the capital's primary, community and continuing care.

The Commission's report estimated that some 15 London acute and SHA hospitals would need to close over the period 1992–2010 to achieve the service rationalisation and re-investment required. Improved efficiency – including major moves to day case procedures in many specialties and shorter lengths of stay – suggested that the hospital service in London could operate with some 5,000 fewer beds by 2010.

- Consolidation of undergraduate and postgraduate medical teaching and research with four major multi-faculty colleges of the University of London – Queen Mary/Westfield, Imperial, University College and King's – with St George's to remain outside.

London Health Care 2010 made clear the Commission's view that these major changes would take some 20 years to implement. With this in mind, the Commission recommended that implementation initially become the responsibility of a dedicated 'task force' with a five-year remit, working with and through all the relevant statutory bodies rather than displacing them.

LIG was charged with overseeing primary care development in the capital. An initial £170 million investment programme for primary care in deprived parts of the capital (the London Initiative Zone – or LIZ) was announced in *Making London Better*. The document announced a 'phased programme of change to bring the pattern of acute sector provision in London more into line with current and future demand' by reducing the number of acute hospital sites, and put forward a 'cautious estimate' of a reduction of 15 to 20 per cent in bed numbers – or some 2,000–2,500 – in four to five years' time.

BOX 2.2: *REPORT OF THE INQUIRY INTO LONDON'S HEALTH SERVICE,*
MEDICAL EDUCATION AND RESEARCH
(CHAIRMAN: PROFESSOR SIR BERNARD TOMLINSON)

The Report of the Inquiry into London's Health Service, Medical Education and Research, which had been commissioned by the then Secretary of State for Health in 1991, was published in 1992. It emphasised the risk of a 'spiral of decline', in which the high unit costs of inner-London hospitals would be exacerbated by the new system of capital charges, with a resulting fall in volumes of cases. It pointed to the risks this would pose for medical education and research and to the need for urgent action to strengthen both in the capital.

Focusing on the five years to 1997, the Tomlinson report made the case for a transfer of resources from acute hospital care to primary care on the grounds that good primary care can substitute for hospital-based provision. The report recommended the development of general medical services in London, through improvements in GP premises and more flexible local contracts, better co-ordination between the organisations responsible for primary care, and an increase in the level of nursing and residential home provision in London, to ease pressure on acute hospitals.

For the acute sector, Tomlinson stated that whole hospital sites would need to close and specialties would need to be rationalised London-wide, if revenue savings were to be achieved. These would be required for re-investment to support service developments elsewhere. Capital receipts from site closures and land sales would be needed to fund acute services reconfigurations. The report anticipated that greater efficiency would mean between 2,000 and 7,000 fewer acute hospital beds in London by 1996/97.

The report pointed out the political and social risks involved if the newly created internal market were allowed to operate unchecked across the capital. It recommended that a limited-life task force be established to 'manage the market' by working with – and between – the existing NHS and higher education structures and the Department of Health.

Making London Better also stated the Government's intention to disaggregate a number of mixed community/acute trusts in inner London in line with the Tomlinson recommendations. It paired major institutions such as Guy's and St Thomas's hospitals and St Bartholomew's and the Royal London, in single trusts explicitly to facilitate site rationalisation. In addition, mergers of medical schools with four multi-faculty colleges of the University of London, identified by both the King's Fund and Tomlinson, were recommended to the Higher Education Funding Council for England.

Implementing change in London

Introducing the changes outlined in *Making London Better* has proved extremely taxing. The next section of this report looks at primary and community care initiatives, medical education and research and the acute hospital sector in turn, to gauge progress. It goes on to consider the policy context in which the London changes have been taking place.

Primary care initiatives

Over the financial years 1993/94–1995/96 £210 million was invested in primary care in the London Initiative Zone (LIZ). The LIZ covered parts of London thought to have high levels of need, where primary care was weak and/or where acute sector rationalisation would increase the pressure on primary care. The aim was 'to improve primary care for London's population and to pave the way for more cost-effective use of London's hospitals' (Department of Health, 1993a). Box 2.3 gives a detailed account of the LIZ initiatives and places them in the context of wider policies for primary care.

The LIZ investment programme had three strands:

- **'getting the basics right',** which involved bringing existing primary care services up to standard through improving premises and attracting better trained staff (62 per cent of projects);
- **developing innovative primary care** by supporting new forms of care in the inner city. These included extended primary care centres, additional staff, services for populations with special needs and GP services in accident and emergency departments (25 per cent of projects);
- **shifting services from hospital to the community** by developing services such as home care, community beds and polyclinics, so that more care could take place outside acute hospitals (13 per cent of projects).

The LIZ programme was established very rapidly in 1993. With oversight from the LIG-sponsored Primary Health Care Forum, plans for 5-year development programmes were established to extremely tight timescales by the 12 LIZ family health services authorities. Inevitably, most relied heavily on pre-existing 'off-the-shelf' projects. In the initial phases, particularly, there was no time to build a coherent local development programme with participation from clinicians, local government and communities.

In 1993/94, the first year of the development programme, 934 projects were initiated in the LIZ, using special funds in addition to the main health authority allocations. These were designed to 'pump-prime' developments, concentrating on the three main objectives of the programme. By 1995/96, more than 1,000 LIZ projects had been sponsored. The majority of LIZ funding has been spent on premises improvements: some 60 per cent of LIZ funding has gone into improving the range and quality of primary care buildings in the zone.

Although the importance of a wide general evaluation was stressed by the LIZ programme, there has been little attempt to assess the impact of LIZ investments as a whole, either against its stated aims in *Making London Better* or in terms of improvements in health outcomes for Londoners. London health authorities are reported to have found it difficult to link developments under the LIZ programme into their primary care strategies and mainstream commissioning, although some have developed evaluation frameworks and criteria to guide future investment.

The speed with which the programme was established gave little or no opportunity for shared learning across participating authorities and practices, and there was little initial support from the Thames regional research and development directorates (Mays *et al.*, 1997). This doubtless contributed to the reported difficulties that LIZ health authorities have had in integrating LIZ schemes within their commissioning strategies.

The LIZ Education Initiative programme (LIZ-EI) funded a partnership between the inner-London local medical committees (LMCs), family health services authorities and academic departments of general practice to offer a range of educational opportunities for general practitioners in the LIZ area between 1995 and 1998. LIZ-EI projects to support undergraduate education and vocational training for GPs have been developed through LIZ health authorities working with academic departments of general practice. LIZ-EI has provided an unprecedented opportunity for GPs in inner London to receive support and funding for their further education. Few individuals in the NHS have received support of this kind, which is all the more unusual, given the fact that GPs are independent contractors. A formal evaluation of the LIZ-EI programme is being undertaken to assess the extent to which it has improved the recruitment and retention of GPs in the inner city. This will be available at the end of the programme (Morley *et al.*, 1997).

LIZ achievements

The scale of LIZ investments in primary care premises and staff seems likely to have a positive impact on the environment in which primary care takes place and on the potential for extending primary health care teams in the capital. The impact that these have had on the quality of primary care available to Londoners remains unclear, however. The fact remains that London is the only major city in England with significant numbers of sub-standard primary care

Box 2.3: LIZ PRIMARY CARE DEVELOPMENT PROJECTS

Getting the basics right

Capital projects

A large proportion (46 per cent) of expenditure was on capital projects. Tomlinson identified premises as a key issue for primary care provision in London, and, per project, a capital project will have a higher cost than a service project. In many places FHSAs chose to use improvement grants, as this offered more flexibility in the overall management of their capital. Improvement grants have also been made available to supplement cost-rent schemes, although this is technically not allowed under current regulations. This has had an added attraction to both managers and practices in that it has meant that longer-term revenue effects of the development are less likely to impact in a major way on either the later years of the programme or cash-limited budgets.

Core primary care staff and services

The second largest area of expenditure was on core primary care staff and services. Inner London previously had low levels of GP support staff. The intention was to bring support for London primary care up to the same level as elsewhere in the country.

Primary care organisation

There are some areas which show less expenditure than expected. Expenditure on the organisation of primary care projects amounted to only 1 per cent of the total. The management of primary care is now seen as a major factor in determining a practice's ability to develop as an effective provider and purchaser of services. The figure shown here may, however, be low because practice management development has been subsumed into both professional development and core primary care staff.

Innovative primary care

Sixteen per cent of expenditure is related to a number of smaller projects identified as 'innovative primary care'. These break down into a wide range of projects, including enhanced general medical services (health promotion, nursing midwifery, cardiac rehabilitation), practice-based additional services (chiropody, physiotherapy, dentistry, speech therapy) and a significant proportion (5 per cent) of mental health projects.

Shifting the balance of care

'Substitution' projects account for 16 per cent of expenditure. At the end of the programme it was anticipated new models of primary care would be funded through transferring resources from the secondary sector. This has proved a naive assumption, since resources from hospital services have not been released to fund community developments.

Source: Mays *et al.* (1997); Morley *et al.* (1997)

premises in the late 1990s. Practice staffing levels in London have improved since the early 1990s. Even so – and in contrast to other urban centres – a significant proportion of London practices remain unsupported by practice nurses (Boyle and Hamblin, 1997). While the LIZ programme initially included an element aimed at addressing poor primary care providers, lobbying from professional interests ensured that this part of the programme was quietly dropped.

LIZ-supported schemes such as the introduction of primary care resource centres, hospital-at-home and intensive home nursing to prevent admission to hospital have demonstrated clearly that it is possible to introduce 'innovative' primary and community services familiar in the rest of the country to inner-deprived London. It is, however, notable that only a small proportion of LIZ schemes covered intermediate services, such as rehabilitation or intensive home nursing to avoid admission – an area that both the Tomlinson report and the King's Fund London Commission had highlighted as needing investment in London.

It is unclear how many LIZ service developments will continue with mainstream health authority support, once the pump-priming, non-recurrent LIZ funding ceases in 1998/99. Most London purchasers within the zone are now reporting difficulties or potential difficulties with supporting innovative LIZ-sponsored service developments because of resource constraints. These problems are accentuated by the fact that it has proved extremely difficult to release funding from acute hospital services to support primary and community developments.

It is too soon to make a full assessment of the long-term impact of the LIZ programme on the range and quality of primary and community care available to people living in inner London. Primary and community services in the rest of England have continued to forge ahead, stimulated in many places by the flexibility of fundholding GP practices to extend the range of services offered from local health centres and surgeries. On many indicators, primary care performance in London, although improving, continues to lag behind performance in other parts of England (Boyle and Hamblin, 1997). Fundholding has been slow to develop in much of the capital, and particularly within inner-deprived London, so the impetus it brings to rethinking service provision has been lacking.

Given the discrepancy that existed between London and other English cities in the early 1990s, this continued gap is hardly surprising. Primary care development in London was always destined to be more than a five-year task.

Although the LIZ will leave a useful legacy of premises improvements, the short-term nature of the funding available for service developments and the speed with which the programme was developed significantly weakened its impact. This effect was worsened by the fact that many innovative service developments were too small scale to be cost-effective, especially since releasing resources from hospital-based care has proved to be an intractable problem in many places.

Medical education and research

Of the three strands of development identified by the first King's Fund Commission and by Tomlinson, the most significant progress has been made in reorganisation of the medical schools and postgraduate institutes and their relationship with the University of London. Substantial progress on all the proposed mergers of undergraduate medical schools with multi-faculty colleges has been made. All but two of the capital's medical schools and postgraduate institutes are now formally linked with one of these university centres.

In south-east London, a merger between King's College and the Institute of Psychiatry is planned, to come into effect from 1 August 1997. The development programme for locating the School of Biomedical Sciences for King's College London and the United Medical Schools of Guy's and St Thomas's Hospitals (UMDS) at the Guy's Hospital site at London Bridge has now been approved by the Government under the Private Finance Initiative (PFI). The scheme involves new and refurbished buildings on the Guy's site for King's College London's School of Life and Health Sciences. It is hoped that contracts will be signed during 1997, leading to the formal merger of UMDS and King's in August 1998. A Bill to enable this merger is currently passing through Parliament.

In north-central London, the Institute of Ophthalmology merged with University College London (UCL) and became part of UCL Medical School. The Institute of Child Health merged in a similar manner in 1996 and the Institute of Neurology will do so on 1 August 1997. A Bill has passed through Parliament enabling the merger of the Royal Free Hospital School of Medicine with UCL with the date to be decided by the parties concerned. It is planned for 1998 or 1999. The Eastman Dental Institute is currently affiliated to UCL, and merger of the two is planned in the next two years.

In north-west London, St Mary's Hospital Medical School merged with Imperial College in 1988. This was followed by the National Heart and Lung Institute joining Imperial College on 1 August 1995, the formal date for the establishment of the Imperial College School of Medicine. The Councils of the

Royal Postgraduate Medical School and the Charing Cross and Westminster Medical School agreed to merge their respective institutions with Imperial College on 1 August 1997. A Bill to this effect is currently passing through Parliament.

In east London, in November 1995 St Bartholomew's Medical College, the London Hospital Medical College and Queen Mary and Westfield College merged to become one institution.

Over a five-year period, eight undergraduate medical schools and seven postgraduate institutes have laid plans to re-form within the four designated multi-faculty colleges of University of London. Detailed planning to bring curricula in line with General Medical Council requirements is under way.

Integration on this scale and with this speed is unprecedented in the capital. The proposals for integration – which echoed those of the Flowers report of 1980 and the Todd report of 1968 – went with the grain of thinking within the University of London and the medical schools. Medical academics and researchers were alive to the risks that continuing fragmentation would bring within the increasingly competitive world of international biomedical research. The progress made represents a remarkable achievement for the institutions concerned and for the University of London. The major centres for medical education and biomedical science that are emerging should provide the institutional base required to safeguard London's position as a world-class research and education centre.

This academic regrouping is already influencing the future shape of health services across the capital. The centres are certain to exert a powerful magnetism over the form of specialty and super-specialty configurations in London as they take shape for the next century.

Although progress has been made in better aligning the institutions responsible for medical education and research in the capital, significant capital investment is required to bring it to fruition by concentrating facilities and staff in the new centres. In south-east London, for example, some £150 million is required to bring medical teaching together with biomedical science onto the Guy's Hospital site. At UCL, the Higher Education Funding Council for England (HEFCE), the Wellcome Trust, the Wolfson Foundation and others are contributing the £46 million required to convert the old University College Hospital into a combined teaching and research facility. The further promotion of clinical teaching and research on the Gower Street site requires funding of approximately £100 million to provide a new hospital for UCL Hospitals NHS Trust.

This and the other mergers require capital funding through the PFI – a route that is proving decidedly problematic, as discussed below. Because of this, the Deans of the London medical schools' report to the King's Fund London Commission states that progress on 'the promised new investment in buildings has been largely stalled' (Deans of the Medical Schools of the University of London, 1997).

Changing acute services in London

Moves to consolidate London's hospitals need to be seen in the context of the continuous evolution of hospital services that has been a feature of the NHS over the past 15 years. The concentration of acute services on fewer sites has been a consistent feature of service development as technological changes in service delivery have dramatically increased medical and surgical sub-specialisation and shortened length of hospital stay.

Research undertaken for the Commission shows that the configuration of acute hospital services in London has changed markedly since 1981. Of the 117 sites used for acute services then, 47 had accident and emergency departments, with a further 70 providing acute hospital services without them. Eleven were stand-alone maternity hospitals and some 43 were single-specialty hospitals of one kind or another.

By 1995, accident and emergency services had been consolidated into 34 departments, some of which were on new hospital sites. Of the 70 acute hospitals which had provided services without an accident and emergency department, only 11 remain. Ten of the 11 stand-alone maternity hospitals have transferred to other sites, and the number of single-specialty sites has been almost halved from 43 to 21. Across London, 38 sites once used as acute hospitals are now being used for primary care or for community health services, including mental health (MHA, 1997).

Then, as now, a mix of clinical quality and cost-effectiveness arguments were used to justify these service changes, which have inevitably proved controversial and difficult to achieve at a local level. However, most of the hospitals which closed over this period were the smaller acute hospitals, some with only one or two wards for general medicine or surgery. Little or nothing was done to address the long-standing concentration of specialist providers in inner-deprived London, the comparative underprovision of hospital services in outer London or the fragmentation of specialty and super-specialty services within London's teaching hospitals.

Acute services reconfiguration in London

The *Making London Better* plans to amalgamate specialties and consolidate acute services need to be seen as part of this continuum, but also as moves to rationalise services within London's teaching hospitals – inevitably a politically sensitive area. There were two main strands:

- achieving a better-balanced, clinically- and cost-effective hospital service on fewer sites;
- the concentration and development of specialist services to serve London's population and support medical research.

Site rationalisation

Looking first at site rationalisation, Tomlinson and *Making London Better* recommended a number of trust mergers to facilitate the development of local proposals for acute hospital and specialty rationalisation and site closures. LIG was instrumental in the behind-the-scenes planning of the structures and appointments required to achieve these. It also co-ordinated work on site valuations and redevelopment costing across London.

In east London, St Bartholomew's and the Royal London Hospital became one trust with Queen Elizabeth Hospital for Children and the London Chest Hospital. The Homerton – which had originally been paired with St Bartholomew's – became a separate trust. In south-east London, Guy's and St Thomas's Trusts were merged and the Lewisham Hospital became a trust in its own right. In the north-west, Charing Cross and the Hammersmith Hospital became one trust. LIG acted as a catalyst for the detailed organisational, financial, site and manpower planning required within individual trusts, and supported management consultants to work with the institutions concerned on this.

LIG saw securing the commitment of clinical and academic leaders and the boards and senior managers of the authorities and institutions involved as the key to change, and worked to get these interests on board. To do so, LIG used its access to ministers and its power to provide funds to assist the change programme.

LIG approved subsidies – termed 'transitional relief' – to meet the difference between the prices that purchasers were able to pay and trusts' service costs and, working with the Thames regions, tied these payments to plans to reduce costs through service and site rationalisations. LIG also made some funds available for training, redeployment, early retirement and redundancy to trusts who had firm plans for staff reductions (Nichols, 1997).

LIG's work on site rationalisation culminated with the Secretary of State for Health's announcement of a series of changes to London health care in April 1995. These were:

- the closure of St Bartholomew's Hospital and the transfer of its acute services to the Royal London site as part of a £240 million redevelopment programme to co-locate St Bartholomew's, the London Chest Hospital and Queen Elizabeth Hospital for Children on the Royal London site with associated developments at the Homerton Hospital in Hackney;
- the concentration of Guy's and St Thomas's Trust inpatient services on the St Thomas's site, with Guy's to become a complementary 'planned care' centre in a £92 million development;
- the £35 million redevelopment of Queen Elizabeth's Military Hospital at Woolwich as an NHS district general hospital and the associated closures of the Brook and Greenwich Hospitals;
- the closure of Edgware General Hospital's accident and emergency department and acute medical and surgical services with the development of modern replacement facilities at Barnet General at a cost of £60 million, with complementary developments at the Royal Free and Northwick Park Hospitals, which between them would handle the dispersed accident and emergency and acute medical and surgical caseload.

In taking these difficult, unpopular decisions, the Secretary of State demonstrated the Government's continuing political commitment to change in London. At this time, LIG was wound up, with its functions for supporting primary care development in London passing to a specially convened Primary Care Support Force. Further progress on the *Making London Better* agenda is now the responsibility of the North and South Thames Regional Offices of the NHS Executive which assumed responsibility for 'transitional relief' funding through their trust units, and of London health authorities and trusts.

To date, some 13 major capital schemes across London have been developed that can be explicitly linked to the *Making London Better* agenda. The six critical schemes, and current progress on them, are listed in Table 2.1. However, obtaining the capital required to fund them has proved extremely difficult.

Initially, there was commitment to public funding for schemes where they could demonstrate benefits in terms of land sales and reduced revenue costs (Nichols, 1997). During 1994/95, however, it became clear that all capital schemes would need to be tested for suitability under the PFI. Effectively, this meant that trusts were required to begin the process of obtaining capital anew, to fresh rules. For those involved, this has meant the frustration of 'learning by doing' as the details of the PFI process have been worked out, complex contracts and funding schemes with private sector consortia arranged, and Treasury approvals sought. Delays are running at at least two years in most cases. Funding for smaller mental health and primary care schemes has all but evaporated.

The uncertainties involved have raised substantial questions about the achievability of the *Making London Better* programme. Moreover, the inflation of costs associated with PFI schemes in London and elsewhere suggests that the revenue savings originally promised by site rationalisations may be appreciably compromised. There is increasing uncertainty about whether London purchasers will in practice be able to fund the expensive services to be provided, as their resources diminish in line with central government allocation formulae (Meara, 1997). As delays continue, the need for continued subsidies to London's providers has increased. During 1995/96 the financial position of London trusts deteriorated markedly, with London providers overall in deficit after interest and Public Dividend Capital payments had been made.

Specialty rationalisation

The Tomlinson report recommended a review of London's cardiac, renal, children's, neurosciences, cancer and plastic surgery services. These reviews were set in train during the spring of 1993, and reported back in June of the same year. Careful attention was paid to the clinical leadership of these reviews: in every case they were chaired by an eminent practitioner in the relevant specialty from outside the capital. Chief executives of the inner-London health authorities acted as their secretaries.

Taken together, the six reviews advocated the establishment of a 'network' of specialty provision across the capital (London Implementation Group, 1993a, 1993b, 1993c, 1993d, 1993e, 1993f). This would involve a limited number of 'hubs' providing the full range of specialist facilities for populations of between 1 and 2 million people. These would relate to a group of 'spoke' hospitals. 'Spokes' would actively collaborate with the specialist centres and take responsibility for routine care locally. While the recommendations were intentionally service-based, they also took explicit account of the need to concentrate specialised procedures and treatments in a limited number of centres to support high calibre research.

The 'hub-and-spoke' network proposed by the specialty reviews marked a move away from the traditional institutionally-based focus of health care planning in London. Their recommendations recognised that increasing clinical specialisation and sub-specialisation meant that it was becoming unrealistic for each and every teaching hospital and district general hospital to aspire to doing everything required for patient treatment and care within their own walls. Two

Table 2.1 Major London PFI schemes

NHS Trust	Greenwich Healthcare	Guy's & St Thomas's	King's Healthcare	Royal Hospitals	University College London Hospitals	Wellhouse
Host Purchaser	Bexley and Greenwich HA	Lambeth Southwark and Lewisham HA	Lambeth Southwark and Lewisham HA	East London and the City HA	Camden & Islington HA	Barnet HA
Scheme	Development of Queen Elizabeth Military Hospital site as acute general hospital for Greenwich	Create acute and tertiary care centre at St Thomas's and planned care centre at Guy's so that sites are complementary	Re-investment in King's site to improve quality and operational efficiency	Co-locate four hospitals on the Royal London site	Co-locate four hospitals on one site	Redevelopment of Barnet General Hospital & dispersal of caseload from Edgware General Hospital
Cost	£35m	£92m	£79m	£240m	£115m	£50m
Hospital Sites to Close	The Brook (closed) and Greenwich DGH	No total closure but a large part of the Guy's site will be vacated	Dulwich Hospital (part)	St Bartholomew's London Chest Queen Elizabeth Hospital for Children, Hackney	Middlesex Hospital Elizabeth Garrett Anderson/Soho & Hospital for Tropical Diseases	Part of Edgware General site
Saving	Cost of LIG support and Greenwich HA loss of income	Cope with reduction of 7% in elective and 5% in non-elective work	c. £8m of value benefit	c. £30m	c. £20m	c. £12m
Objectives	• Develop QEMH site • Close/dispose of Brook site • Close/dispose of Greenwich DGH • Provide residential accommodation • Overall reduction in beds	• Creation of women and children's centre, cancer centre and renal centre at St Thomas's • Refurbishment and adaptation at St Thomas's • Creation of planned care centre at Guy's • Outpatient and patient hotel at St Thomas's • Disposal of part of Guy's site to King's UMDS • Dispose of Lambeth Hospital site • Development of private patient services • Overall reduction in beds	• Centralise services on one site • Create internally configured site based on patient focused and 'transformation' principles • Close Dulwich site • Overall reduction in beds	• Develop Royal London site at Whitechapel • Close Bart's, Q.E. Hospital for Children and London Chest hospitals • Redesign patient flows within the new hospital • Create more flexible inpatient accommodation • Overall reduction in beds • Relocate some services from Mile End Hospital to Royal London site • Integrate clinical/teaching/research campus	• Develop single site • Close Middlesex EGA/Soho & Hospital for Tropical Diseases sites • Provide flexible facilities that are accessible to patients and in one place • Enable co-location of women's services • Overall reduction in beds	• Complete redevelopment of Barnet General • Transfer of services from Edgware General • Possible closure of part of Edgware site • Overall reduction in beds

Note: This table is based on the position as of January 1997 (Meara, 1997) strategic developments were implied: concentration of scarce skills and expensive equipment and the development of relationships between specialist centres and local hospitals and primary care to ensure access to care of a high standard.

The detailed recommendations of the specialty reviews are summarised in Appendix 5, along with an account of progress to date on enacting them. These involved specific recommendations about the future of particular clinical departments and/or institutions. Little detail was given on either the respective functions of the 'hubs' and 'spokes', or the relationships between the two components of the proposed system.

The unusually tight timescale within which the reviews were produced meant that professional and managerial contributions to their recommendations were necessarily restricted. There was very little co-ordination across the reviews, which meant that, overall, their recommendations lacked consistency. Opportunities for public debate on either proposed models and their implications or on the changes recommended for individual institutions were also extremely limited. LIG did, however, sponsor a series of seminars for clinicians and user representatives on each of the reviews in the month following their publication (Farrell, 1993).

The review recommendations were fed into the site rationalisation and NHS business planning processes described above. LIG continued its work as a behind-the-scenes catalyst of the organisational and medico-political processes required to implement the changes recommended for particular institutions and clinical departments.

However, it is now clear that the impetus to rationalise specialties largely faltered following the publication of the reviews. The set of changes to London health care announced by the Secretary of State in April 1995 concentrated exclusively on acute hospital site reconfiguration: the recommendations of the specialty reviews did not feature in the decisions announced at that time.

In effect, the specialty reviews' recommendations have been largely frustrated by institutions to which they posed a threat. This possibility was indicated very early when the Secretary of State declared that Harefield Hospital would stay open, contrary to the recommendations of the cardiac review. This gave a signal that all potential changes were back in the melting pot. London's teaching hospitals are adept in the micro- and macro-politics of protecting their institutional interests (Rivett, 1986). From 1993 onwards, their tactical skills have been deployed adroitly to ward off general service rationalisations through departmental mergers or closures (Towell *et al.*, 1997).

In many instances, London's purchasers worked with local provider interests to prevent change. They were encouraged to do so by the risk that they would experience increases in prices if departments within local hospitals closed, as a result of fixed costs being spread across a lower volume of activity. Where specialty rationalisations have been approved, their implementation frequently requires capital funding. This now depends upon the PFI, as Appendix 5 describes.

Alienation of Londoners

Slow progress with PFI funding relates to a fundamental shortcoming of the past five years: the failure to convince Londoners of the need for changes to their health care system. Initially, both *London Health Care 2010* and the Tomlinson report were well received by NHS policy-makers and many commentators in the professional and quality press. There was a view from within the Service and the University of London that change was overdue – although London's shortcomings in terms of primary and continuing care raised questions about the speed with which acute bed reductions could be made (Jarman, 1994).

Inevitably, as the implications of change for individual institutions and clinical teams became clearer, resistance among the public and the staff of threatened institutions grew. Hospitals are powerful symbols for local communities. They are also major local employers. Particularly when closure of accident and emergency departments were involved, ministers, the NHS Executive, London health authorities and trusts became embroiled in battles with the capital's MPs, media, community health councils, local authorities, health unions and a highly sceptical public over the shape and scope of service reconfigurations. Positive messages about investments in primary and community services under the LIZ programme have been eclipsed.

The protracted and unsatisfactory nature of formal NHS public consultation processes has intensified these confrontations. Widespread anxiety about the PFI, the delays associated with it and its ability to deliver the capital needed for modernisation at an acceptable price has heightened public unease. 'Planning blight' and disillusion with the change process have been the result among the public and some groups of NHS staff.

Five years on, it is clear that the quality, service and economic arguments in favour of change have failed to persuade key stakeholders – most particularly Londoners themselves. As a result, what the first London Commission saw as a programme of essential modernisation is perceived by some as wholesale destruction of services already under intense pressure.

Conclusion

A mixed picture on implementation has emerged in the four years since *Making London Better* was put forward as the Government's response to the Tomlinson report.

Through the LIZ programme, some £250 million will have been spent on developing primary and community services in London between 1993 and 1998. While it is too early to assess its full effects, it is clear that the LIZ investment programme has resulted in significant investment in practice premises, staffing and GP training. A much smaller proportion of money has been spent on addressing London's deficits in rehabilitation and continuing care. The long-term impact of innovative schemes to substitute primary and community health services for hospital care is in doubt, because many will not continue to be funded.

However, although there have been improvements over the last four years, primary care in London still continues to lag behind comparable areas of other English cities in the range of general medical services it provides, and in its performance on childhood immunisation, cervical cytology and other national targets (Boyle and Hamblin, 1997; Morley *et al.*, 1997). The speed with which the LIZ programme was established, and the relative absence of developmental support at its initial stages, have also limited its impact.

Progress on changes in acute services is disappointing. Despite sustained political backing for a controversial change programme, and considerable planning at local level by London trusts and health authorities, progress on rationalising hospital sites and specialties has stalled. Institutional resistance and delays in accessing capital through the PFI are largely responsible for this. Delays in implementing rationalisation and closure plans have contributed to the alienation of Londoners and – in some instances – NHS staff groups from the change programme.

The institutional integration of London's medical schools and postgraduate institutes with the multi-faculty colleges of the University of London is the outstanding achievement of the last five years. However, progress on their physical integration depends on large-scale capital programmes which also require PFI funding. It remains to be seen whether – and when – this will become available.

CHAPTER 3

Changing London

Introduction

Wider social, economic, political and technological changes influence both the demands for health care and the way they are met. Both nationally and internationally, a number of influences impinge on the health service system. Many of these forces are well known, but contradictions and paradoxes between them mean that their ultimate effects remain hard to predict. Taken together, they are forcing a restructuring of health service systems internationally.

The changes discussed in the previous chapter need to be understood within this wider national and international context. Their impact will inevitably be filtered through the existing service system and the major changes to British health and social policy of recent years.

This chapter examines national and international trends, looks at recent changes to British health policy, and discusses the impact of both of these on health care in London over the last five years. It goes on to look at the recent evidence of health and social services activity in London. Finally, it identifies significant strains within the service system that require urgent policy attention.

International trends

Changing attitudes to health and health care

Attitudes to health have changed. People have become much better informed about their own health and about health care. Increasingly, people are actively involved in their own health, and in their treatment when they are ill.

This relates to wider social changes: professional judgements are no longer accepted uncritically, and hierarchies of all kinds are being questioned. People are requesting improvements in the information they receive about their care.

As medical technology has expanded what health care has to offer, people are becoming more discriminating about the services they use. Increasingly, user groups are seeking to influence the style and setting of services. In the UK, the care of people with HIV/AIDS and maternity services has already been significantly influenced by user preferences.

NHS policy reflects this major social trend. Responsiveness to patients is one of the three top-level objectives for the service as a whole. Initiatives like *The*

Patient's Charter and national waiting-list targets have placed new emphasis on users' rights and preferences. In future, user views are likely to shape the style of service delivery, and individual users will play a much more active part in their own care. NHS service design and delivery will need to become much more skilled at responding to the diverse requirements of individuals and communities.

Changed expectations about what health care can offer are one of the reasons why demand for services has escalated during the 1990s. Along with their counterparts elsewhere in the country, health authorities and trusts in London have been struggling with rising numbers of emergency admissions and increasing demands for care.

Demographic changes

Ageing London

The 'ageing' of advanced industrialised countries is well recognised, as is its corollary: the existence of increasing numbers of frail older people in need of care. It remains uncertain whether current patterns of limiting long-term illness and disability in old age will persist, or whether older people will in future stay fitter longer – or become more infirm in the last years of life (Harrison *et al.*, 1997).

Over the next 20 years, the numbers of people aged over 75 in London will rise less steeply than in the rest of the UK, although they will grow slightly (Boyle and Hamblin, 1997). Since older people are major users of health services, this will place growing demands on the NHS. Older people's slower physiological and psychological rate of recovery from illness and from medical interventions must increasingly be taken into account when health services are designed (Stocking, 1992).

Ethnic diversity

In the years to 2010, London's population will become ethnically and culturally even more diverse. This will be true in all age-groups, so that, for the first time, the capital will have an appreciable population of minority ethnic elders. The minority ethnic populations of some London boroughs are already as high as 40 per cent. These proportions will increase steadily, requiring health services to respond positively to a wide range of cultural expectations and community preferences.

Technological change

Technological developments have brought major changes to British health care over the last decade. Minimally invasive techniques have meant a decrease in the length of stay in hospital and a steep rise in day cases. Health care intervention rates have increased dramatically, particularly for older people. Using most conventional measures, the efficiency of hospital services has increased markedly over the period. At the same time, an ever-increasing amount of treatment and care is taking place at home, or in primary and community settings.

The move to day case procedures for elective surgical work has meant a number of changes to the way in which hospitals organise themselves. In many trusts the majority of hospital inpatient stays are now for emergency cases. This means that when emergency admissions increase in the winter months, there is a much reduced complement of surgical beds to be switched to emergency use.

Other developments are in prospect which could exert just as profound an influence. They include:

- **new drugs**, e.g. for osteoporosis and for dementia;
- **genetic diagnosis and therapy**, leading to better and earlier diagnosis or the elimination of certain categories of disease;
- **improvements in monitoring procedures** and more specific drug, vaccine and hormone treatments through biotechnology.

The implications of this for the pattern of health care delivery are difficult to determine. Forces for centralisation and decentralisation are present at the same time, and there are tensions between them (Harrison, 1997).

Some new technologies favour hospitals because of their expense and the complex skills required to deliver them; others – particularly pharmaceutical innovations – will move treatment for certain conditions to patients' homes and to GPs' surgeries (Banta, 1990). The increasing number of frail older people should mean a new emphasis on rehabilitation, recovery and care (Steiner, 1997).

What does seem certain is that technological innovation will continue to expand the range of intervention and modes of care available. This has already blurred traditional distinctions between primary, secondary and tertiary care, and between medical and surgical specialties.

The ever-increasing range and volume of services also pose obvious and well-rehearsed problems for funding health care across the developed world. In Britain, the range of critical choices means that the NHS will have to become much more skilled at determining the most clinically and cost-effective modes of care to respond to the needs and preferences of given populations (Harrison, 1997).

Quality and outcome

The quality of health care has become a more explicit concern of health policy internationally over the last five years. Moves within the NHS to ground clinical practice and service delivery with evidence of effectiveness are a result. Despite significant investment in clinical audit and NHS research and development, the application of effectiveness information to clinical practice is still in its infancy. Apart from *Patient's Charter* indicators, there is very little information, and virtually none on a routine basis, that bears on the quality of care actually on offer within the service (Harrison, 1997). The effectiveness literature has concentrated on particular health care interventions: at present, there is sparse evidence with which to assess the relative effectiveness of health care programmes or different styles of service delivery. This is likely to change, requiring health authorities and trusts to become more discriminating in the choices they make. Social and economic changes, such as increases in patient participation and moves for greater professional accountability, are likely to continue the pressure for increased information on effectiveness and outcomes. Increasingly, that evidence will influence service design and delivery.

More high-quality evaluative research is required if the case for the centralisation of certain kinds of treatment in specialist centres is to be strengthened. There is some evidence to suggest that the best patient outcomes result from expert clinical teams treating a given volume of cases. However, a recent systematic review by the University of York reports as inconclusive the evidence linking volume of activity to better clinical outcomes (University of York, 1997). In the few cases where the relationship between volume and outcome has been clearly demonstrated – for procedures like coronary artery bypass graft or cholecystectomy – they claim, 'the process by which volume may affect quality is poorly understood'.

At the same time, the amount of highly skilled clinical teamwork needed to deliver optimal care for complex conditions is set to increase, along with the cost of the diagnostic and treatment technologies used. These interrelationships can be clearly seen in the way in which transplantation and the field of neonatology have developed over the past 20 years. The increasing complexity of care is resulting in increased specialisation and sub-specialisation within medicine.

The LIG specialty reviews recognised the force of this in their recommendations for London. In general, they concluded that larger units than currently existed were more likely to produce better clinical outcomes, and that these larger centres needed to be more firmly linked to local hospital services and to primary care in order to improve the quality of the complete care programmes available to individual patients (London Implementation Group, 1993a, 1993b, 1993c, 1993d, 1993e, 1993f). At the same time, more coherent connections between the specialties and medical education and research need to be fostered.

More recent national reviews of service areas such as cancer care have taken this thinking much further. Co-ordinated networks of care, based around the concept of the 'patient journey', are the result, with protocol-driven links between each part of the system and transparent quality assurance. Box 3.1 explains this further.

Blurring boundaries

All four of these influences – attitudes, demography, technology and quality – are changing the shape of health care internationally. One notable effect has been to emphasise the interconnections between different parts of the health care system. Demarcations between different forms of care are breaking down, and descriptions like 'primary', 'community' or 'acute' are no longer adequate. Instead, specialties like emergency or cancer care need to be understood as interlocking networks within which different service elements – for example, primary care organisations and general and specialist hospitals – are interdependent. The roles of clinicians are changing too, with traditional distinctions between doctors, nurses and other clinicians subject to negotiation and change. Increasingly, the different elements and actors within the service system must be seen in terms of their contribution to programmes of care for individual people or groups. As such, they need to be able to adapt appropriately to evidence about effectiveness and user preferences as it emerges.

From this comes the recognition that the components of health care need to be understood as a complex interrelated system. Each element is mutable, subject to change and should be planned to complement others. Each is also critically dependent on the wider policy context in which they take place (Harrison, 1997).

The UK policy context

The NHS and Community Care Act 1990

In London, as elsewhere in the UK, the effect of these long-term trends is filtered through the lens of national policy for health and social services. During the 1990s, implementation of the NHS and Community Care Act has been a central preoccupation of UK health policy. Debate on health policies and politics have revolved around NHS structures. The strengths and weaknesses of

Box 3.1: Cancer Services: moving towards networks
of patient-centred care

In May 1995, the Department of Health published *A Policy Framework for Commissioning Cancer Services* (the 'Calman-Hine' Report), setting out the recommendations of an Expert Advisory Group on Cancer brought together by Sir Kenneth Calman and Dr Deirdre Hine (Department of Health, 1995). The group had been established as a result of anxiety among professionals, managers and users about a need to improve cancer services, and a general view that variability in clinical practice and services was unacceptable.

The Calman-Hine Report proposed three 'tiers' of cancer care, forming a co-ordinated network of care:

- **Primary and community-based services,** provided by the members of primary care teams and including health promotion, screening, initial diagnosis, referral for diagnosis and treatment, support for patients and their carers, co-ordination and delivery of palliative care, terminal and bereavement services.

- **Cancer units** based in district general hospitals, having specialist multi-disciplinary teams with the expertise to manage the more common cancers such as breast, lung and bowel. Units are expected to deliver disease-specific care equal to that provided in cancer centres and *not* to be in any way second class units. Cancer units will be attached to cancer centres and will provide care according to protocols agreed with the cancer centre to which they relate.

- **Cancer centres** based in large hospitals and providing more high-technology facilities which will be needed by some patients. Cancer centres are expected to provide centralised and specialised expertise in the management and treatment of the majority of cancers.

The report emphasises the need for clear links, based on protocols, between the different tiers of cancer care. The focus is on networks of people rather than on buildings, focused on delivering high quality, co-ordinated care. The report also emphasises the importance of cancer centres being patient-centred, providing access to a good primary care team, and appropriate information, support and assistance.

For individual clinicians and teams to receive 'Calman-Hine accreditation', regional office cancer teams and local purchasers are seeking assurance that sufficient numbers of cancer procedures are carried out by the individual clinician or trust. This is leading to significant shifts of cancer work between clinicians and between hospitals, particularly in the surgical specialties. For example, in general surgery, consultants are being designated as breast surgeons, colorectal surgeons, and vascular surgeons, in contrast to their former designation as 'general surgeons'.

This is forcing groups of specialties to work together in new ways, with a service such as head and neck cancer drawing together ear, nose and throat surgery, clinical oncology, radiotherapy, MRI imaging and plastic surgery into a common set of protocols for a single clinical team. Increasingly, groups of professionals are being organised around a 'patient journey' or care pathway, rather than on strictly departmental lines.

Source: Ham *et al.* (1997)

the UK 'internal market' for state-supported health care have been a consistent focus for controversy.

Work on the change programme defined in *Making London Better* has run in parallel with the introduction of the 1990 Act. The London changes of the last five years are intimately bound up with the 'purchaser/provider' split and the establishment of the NHS internal market. Indeed, for practical purposes it is frequently impossible to disentangle the effects of the two sets of policies.

Making London Better saw the decentralising of decision-making to individual purchasers and providers through the internal market as the main mechanism for effecting change in the capital. LIG was always intended to be a temporary body and was in fact wound up in less than its allotted time. London health authorities, trusts and the two Thames regional offices of the NHS Executive are the organisations chiefly responsible for implementing the London change agenda, with University of London and the capital's local authorities playing an important role outside the health service.

Purchaser and provider structures in London

The 1990 Act established purchaser and provider structures within the NHS and local authority social services departments. All London's NHS hospital and community health services are provided by NHS trusts, including those of the previously free-standing Special Health Authorities. From April 1996 the four Thames regions became two regional offices of the NHS Executive. The 29 London district health authorities and 16 family health services authorities merged to form 16 London health authorities.

London's 32 boroughs, and the City of London, also introduced internal purchaser and provider arrangements within their social services departments in order to implement the community care sections of the 1990 Act from April 1993.

The 1990 Act also gave GP practices who fulfilled specific organisational and financial criteria the option of becoming GP fundholders (GPFHs). In early phases of fundholding, GPFHs took over the purchasing of some planned investigations and treatments for their practice populations. The range was later extended and community health services were added. More recently, the scheme has evolved to permit smaller practices to participate. There are now different modes of GP fundholding, including total purchasing pilots, where GPFHs purchase a much wider range of emergency and elective care (Mays and Dixon, 1996).

Fundholding was slow to take off in London and remains relatively poorly developed in the capital. There are areas where it is strongly represented, such as Kingston and Richmond, but there are comparatively few fundholders in inner London. This is largely expained by the relative underdevelopment of general practice and the concentration of small practices in these areas.

Devolving decision-making

Underlying these new structures was the notion of developing a market in health provision in which health authorities and GPFHs would decide what to purchase, and from whom. They were given an explicit responsibility for assessing local needs, determining service strategies and specifications, and purchasing accordingly. Health authorities were also given responsibility for 'managing the market' in their local patch and – where dictated by local needs and circumstances – developing new providers and new forms of service.

As such, the 1990 changes involved an explicit decentralisation of decision-making to the local level. The old regional health authorities' ability to determine service developments and investment through their control of NHS capital had no place in the new system. Accordingly, a wide range of regional health authority functions, including specialty planning and responsibility for non-medical education and training, were devolved to local health authorities.

Funding long-term care

The NHS and Community Care Act 1990 gave local authority social services departments responsibility for funding and arranging care and support for people with disabilities, including long-term residential care. This policy change – which was designed to contain expenditure previously committed through the social security budget – introduced a new institutional boundary for hospital discharges.

Previously, the open-ended nature of the residential care budget meant that hospitals could effectively make whatever transfers they wished, subject to Department of Social Security rules on income and assets. From 1993 this could not be assumed: a new boundary with local authority social services must now be negotiated to arrange discharges (Harrison, 1997). In many parts of London this has proved decidedly problematic, with significant numbers of hospital discharges delayed until social services funding for placements or care packages becomes available.

As a result, the interdependence of the health and social care systems for supporting people with long-term disabilities now has greater salience. Frail older people and people with mental health problems are perhaps particularly affected. Responsibility for the funding and provision of their care is split between local government and the NHS, with the risk that it becomes a focus for attempts to shift costs between agencies. The introduction of local health authority eligibility criteria for continuing NHS care in 1996 has reinforced the division between health and social care and increased the risk that individuals will end up in the no man's land between local authority and health authority funding criteria.

Changes to workforce and training policies

Numbers of medical staff have increased steadily in recent years, but reports of shortages in a number of specialties are increasingly common. Paediatrics, geriatrics and psychiatry provide current examples in London. This is despite the fact that a proportionately greater number of consultants and junior medical staff are employed in NHS trusts in inner London. The origins of these staffing problems lie, at least in part, with centrally driven changes to medical education and training.

Two separate NHS policies are coming together to reshape post-registration medical education for future hospital consultants. Both policies will result in marked changes to the delivery of care to patients and in the reshaping of some clinical services. As a consequence, new working patterns are being introduced and old working relationships reshaped. The first policy is the 'New Deal' for junior doctors with its shorter working hours. The second, put forward by the Chief Medical Officer, Sir Kenneth Calman, and supported by the Royal Colleges, is the shorter, more structured educational programme leading to a certificate of completion of medical training. Box 3.2 summarises the impact of these policies on the hospital service.

The result of both policies will be a shorter, more intense period of clinical work for doctors in training, with longer periods set aside for education. A second intended consequence of the two policies is that more care will be delivered to patients by fully trained medical staff – that is, by consultants. Full implementation of the policies will require more consultants: however, in many specialties there are too few doctors in the training grade to fill the posts available – hence the staff shortages discussed above.

The 'Calman' changes are still working through the system, but they are certain to generate increased costs. The impact on London has not been quantified, but estimates for the Oxford and Anglia Region put the cost there at some £20 million. Smaller trusts will have to consider changes to traditional patterns of medical staffing to contain costs, or face the possibility that they will no longer be able to support the medical staffing costs of the smaller clinical specialties. Primary/secondary/tertiary 'networks' and variations on the 'hub-and-spoke' model will be needed to maintain local access to specialist care (Ham *et al.*, 1997).

BOX 3.2: CHANGES TO NHS WORKFORCE AND TRAINING POLICY

Developments in workforce and training policy are forcing significant changes to the working lives of senior hospital doctors. Consultants are experiencing new patterns of working, including a greater involvement in out-of-hours and direct clinical work. Junior doctors are working shorter hours but often on a more intensive basis. They are required to develop more structured 'handover' between shifts to assure continuity of care. Junior doctors are following structured training programmes based on objective performance criteria, backed up by formal mentorship, supervision and appraisal. This is leading to a new requirement for consultants to be taught how to train.

The consultant 'firm' is giving way to larger teams of consultants. Clinical specialties are being reconfigured into new relationships. General specialties are splitting into sub-specialties and many specialties are being linked together into networks organised around the concept of the 'patient journey'. Nurses and other staff are using the opportunities of changes in medical staffing to develop a significant range of new skills and competences. This requires training and resources.

These developments have important implications:

- There is a need to integrate medical workforce planning with the business planning activity and cycles of all trusts.

- This substitution of technologies, locations and staff is a particular challenge to the district general hospital. General hospitals are likely increasingly to become part of networks of total care, linked with regional centres and primary care-based services.

- Changes to medical staffing and training will affect the nature and distribution of hospitals in the future. Smaller hospitals may either become staffed entirely by specialists, staff grade doctors and GPs or they may form alliances and networks with larger units. These hospitals may become part of integrated care organisations.

- The network or 'hub-and-spoke' model offers a way of maintaining local access to services and ensuring the delivery of high quality care. This may involve, as a minimum, collaboration between clinicians, but more ambitiously, it could lead to the merging of management arrangements and ultimately a reduction in the number of NHS trusts. Different arrangements are likely to emerge in different parts of the country and trust mergers are only one option.

A major test for the NHS is its ability to respond intelligently to these developments in an environment where the need for change is not well understood by the general public and where there is often opposition to proposed alterations to the use and configuration of hospitals.

Source: Ham *et al.* (1997)

In many smaller trusts, the 'Calman' changes are acting as a spur to rethinking the way in which medical staff have traditionally been organised and deployed within hospitals. The organisation of medical and surgical 'firms' and traditional demarcations between medical and nursing roles are a particular focus for experimentation and innovation, although as yet there has been little attempt at national or regional level to examine the effects of this and its implications for future education and training (Oxford and Anglia Regional Office, 1997).

Increasing numbers of doctors are choosing to work in hospitals after the end of their pre-registration year. The numbers of doctors opting for general practice has fallen dramatically and there are many places on vocational training schemes in general practice which are unfilled.

London, with 60 per cent more consultants and 40 per cent more doctors in training grades relative to the population than the rest of England, should be better placed to meet the challenge of changes in post-registration medical education. However, it is not clear if there is the flexibility and co-operation between trusts and between consultants needed to enable a smooth transition to the new system.

Changes to research and development funding mechanisms

Approximately half the total national funds for medical research go to London's universities, medical schools and NHS trusts involved in research and development. London's present strength in funds received is also a potential weakness. In the recent Higher Education Funding Council for England Research Assessment Exercise, although London's postgraduate research institutions did very well, only one group of departments in one London medical school achieved a 5 rating and none the top 5*.

By comparison, Oxford and Cambridge each achieved 5*s and 5s in all three units of assessment. Overall, the London medical school average was no better than the average for the rest of the country.

Considerations of medical research excellence are important for the future financial well-being of London hospitals associated with the University. The NHS has an obligation to provide facilities to enable research to be done within the clinical service framework. The funding for research in the NHS was reviewed by the Culyer Task Force which reported in 1994 (Department of Health, 1994). Culyer recommended that an exercise be undertaken to identify all the research and costs incurred by the NHS in supporting it. This was carried out in 1996 and revealed the extent of the subsidy by the NHS to research in London – £189.9 million in North Thames and £48.6 million in South Thames – 71 per cent of the total for the NHS in England.

In some provider units in London, especially the former Special Health Authority hospitals, but also the main teaching hospitals, this funding is a substantial proportion of income. Under the new financial system for NHS research and development which will operate from 1998/99, provider units will have to bid in competition for funding for the support of their clinical research. Although initially the funding base for individual provider units is not likely to change rapidly, the explicit intention of the new system is to redistribute resources in the UK according to NHS research priorities, and to those units best able to do high quality research.

A proportion of the teaching and research and development money that supports London hospitals is therefore 'at risk' under the new arrangements. The new system has been designed to buffer the effects of any changes to research and development funding on service costs, but it is not clear whether this distinction will remain watertight. The potential for some sums of research and development and/or education money to shift both within the capital and between London and the rest of the country now exists in a way that is new.

At the same time, the Service Increment for Teaching (SIFT) has been extended to encompass primary care. Once again, the effect of these changes is still being worked through. However, over the next five years SIFT money will shift from the hospital to the community, to support a wider pattern of medical teaching within primary care settings. This could well have a destabilising effect on hospitals' finances.

Taken together, changes to the funding of NHS research and development and clinical education are substantial. The long-term effects on the NHS in London remains an open question, although it is clear that a new potential for destabilising institutions has been introduced.

Deregulating primary care

The NHS (Primary Care) Act 1997 ends general practitioners' monopoly on the provision of primary health care while preserving the right of everyone to register with an individual family doctor and to receive this service free of charge. The new Act permits local health authorities to suspend GPs' and other independent contractors' contracts – which are negotiated nationally – and allows more flexible arrangements, designed to meet specific local needs. Initially, this will be done on a pilot basis.

GPs and dentists who wish to can become salaried employees of NHS trusts instead of being independent contractors working in small partnerships. This could mean the development of new primary care organisations much larger than the traditional GP partnership, with increased capacity for providing a range of diagnosis, assessment and treatment in primary care settings and of linking effectively with social services.

Using the new legislation to improve services for Londoners will be particularly difficult because of long-standing problems with primary care in the capital (see below). Potentially, however, the Act gives the capital's health authorities a new lever with which to address variable quality across the city.

Special characteristics of London's health care system

London's health care system operates in the same policy environment as the rest of Britain's, but some of its features are distinctive. In a number of important respects it is more diverse and complex than health care in any other part of the country. In particular, London has:

- a population which is extremely ethnically and socially diverse, making the identification of health needs a critical process;
- a concentration of groups with particularly intense needs, such as mentally disordered offenders;
- poorly developed primary care compared to the rest of the country, with substantial variation in the quality of provision both between individual practices and between sectors of London;
- overlapping hospital catchment areas, resulting in a greater degree of competition between institutions than elsewhere;
- trusts which gain a considerable proportion of their income from purchasers outside their own district, so that there are strong interconnections between different parts of London, and purchaser power is relatively diluted;
- trusts in inner London which gain a greater proportion of their income from medical education and research and development than their counterparts in other parts of the country – this is especially true for the former SHAs;
- providing and purchasing structures which vary considerably between different parts of the capital: GP fundholding is very weak in inner London, and acute hospital services are organised differently across the city – there is no one model of care;
- most health authorities and trusts dealing with a multiplicity of local authorities, making the boundary between NHS- and social services-funded provision particularly complex;
- patient flows across the capital resulting in London health authorities having unusually complex contract portfolios.

In the sections that follow, health and social services activity data for London are analysed to illustrate these general points. From this, a sense of the complexity of health and social care provision emerges, along with an appreciation of the variation between different parts of the capital. Boxes 3.3 to 3.7 give a sense of the diversity of health and social services delivery patterns across the city.

Health and social services activity in London

Primary and community services

General practice

Information on general practice in London prepared for the first King's Fund Commission suggested that a poorer range and quality of provision was available to Londoners than in the rest of England, with primary care in London performing less well than in equivalent parts of other English cities. London also had markedly higher proportions of older, single-handed practitioners and poorer GP premises. Performance on a range of indicators – for example, immunisations, cervical cytology and provision of minor surgery – was significantly worse than comparable parts of the country and the average for England.

At that time, expenditure on family health services per capita resident population in London was equivalent to the England average, but less than in other comparable English cities. Within this, the balance of spending was different, with more being spent on general medical services and less on pharmaceutical services. In London, a higher proportion of GPs' income was derived from capitation and deprivation payments and a lower proportion from service payments than the rest of the country (Boyle and Smaje, 1993).

Five years on, the condition of London GPs' practice premises remains poor overall, with considerable variation between different parts of the capital. Forty-five per cent of premises are considered to be below minimum standard in the east of the city compared with 14 per cent in the south. In 1994/95, a quarter of all practice premises in London were below minimum standards. This continues to compare poorly with the rest of England, where just 2 per cent fall below minimum standards.

There has been an overall improvement in the standard of premises since 1992/93, but the position has deteriorated since 1990/91 when just 20 per cent of GP premises in London were considered to be below minimum standards. This apparent discrepancy may be explained by changes in health authority reporting on premises' standards since 1990/91. However, given the long lead times required for capital projects, it is also likely that the effects of the LIZ investments in practice premises have yet to be fully realised.

London as a whole has a similar number of GPs per capita resident population when compared to the rest of England. However, there are more GPs per capita in inner-deprived London than in comparable areas in other English cities. London as a whole has twice the number of single-handed GPs as the rest of England – 20 per cent compared with 9 per cent. This proportion has not changed markedly since 1990/91. The proportion of GPs who practice single-handedly varies across the capital and ranges from 13 per cent in the south to 25 per cent in the east. London also continues to have a higher proportion of GPs aged over 65 than other parts of the country.

Probably as a result of the poor overall standard of GP premises and the relatively high proportion of single-handed GPs, a higher proportion of GPs in London are without a practice nurse – 14 per cent for London compared to 4 per cent in the rest of England. However, the position has improved since 1991/92, when 25 per cent of London practices were without a practice nurse.

London now has slightly more practice staff per GP than other parts of the country – a change from 1990/91 when it had slightly fewer. 'Other practice staff' include chiropodists, counsellors, physiotherapists, and clerical and managerial staff. Given the skills that 'other practice staff' bring to general practices, they can enhance the range of services offered in primary care. There is considerable variation across London in the number of 'other practice staff' per GP, from 1.6 in the north-central sector to 2.6 in the south-east.

GPs in London continue to perform less well against national targets for immunisation and screening than those in the rest of England. London GPs also provide child health surveillance to proportionately fewer children than their counterparts in the rest of the country. Fifty-eight per cent of London children under five receive child health surveillance compared to an average of 76 per cent in the rest of the country. Child health surveillance covers developmental monitoring, including hearing and sight tests.

Figure 3.1 shows that in other English cities there is no performance gradient across different types of socio-economic area for child health surveillance. Outside London, over 70 per cent of children under five are checked regardless of the socio-economic characteristics of the area they live in. In the capital, a lower proportion of children in inner-deprived areas receive checks than those living in high-status areas. Surveillance rates also vary across different parts of the capital: GP practices in north London screen significantly fewer children than their south London counterparts.

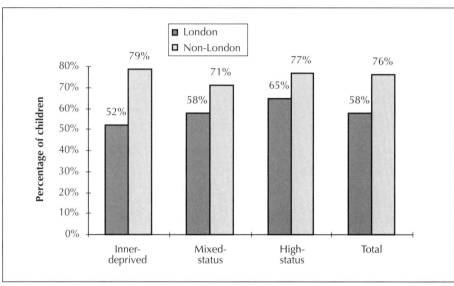

Source: Boyle and Hamblin (1997)

Figure 3.1 Provision of child health surveillance, London and England, 1994/95

The evidence suggests that while the range and quality of services available to Londoners from general practice have improved since 1990/91, they still lag behind those available in the rest of England and in comparable English cities. In London as a whole, a much lower proportion of GPs provide minor surgery than is the case in the rest of England – 56 compared with 85 per cent. Fewer than half the GPs in east London are on the minor surgery list. Provision of minor surgery in London has increased since 1990/91. Yet even Bromley Health Authority – which at 78 per cent has the highest proportion of GPs on the minor surgery list in the capital – has a lower proportion than the national average. Since GPs must meet health authority eligibility criteria relating to training, premises and staffing to be included on their district's minor surgery list, it is likely that London's relatively slow progress towards these criteria is a reflection of persistent general problems.

Overall, general practice in London performs less well than the rest of the country against all performance targets, and this is especially true of inner-deprived parts of the capital. However, it is striking that even high-status areas of London perform less well than inner-deprived areas of other English cities.

Some of this variation between London and the rest of the country may be explained by the mobility of the London population, which is greater than elsewhere. There is evidence for this in the greater number of new registrations and registration health checks with GPs per 1,000 resident population in London, particularly in inner-deprived parts of the capital, compared to their counterparts in the rest of England. However, the evidence also suggests that the vicious circle of poor premises, more limited skills and fewer clinical and support staff first identified in the Acheson report on London's primary care continues to limit the services available to Londoners (Acheson, 1981).

For pharmaceutical services, 4 per cent fewer prescriptions are dispensed per capita than in the rest of England. For inner-deprived London the difference with comparable parts of other English cities is more marked, with 24 per cent fewer prescriptions. However, the relative position of London and England has changed since 1990/91. The number of prescriptions dispensed in London has increased by 18 per cent over the last five years, compared to 8 per cent nationally.

As in 1990/91, per capita expenditure on family health services in London seems low when compared to the rest of England. Once again, London's position compared with the rest of England masks relatively higher expenditure on general medical services and lower spending on pharmaceuticals.

Overall, therefore – and despite improvements in some aspects of provision – it is clear that services available from London's general practices continue to lag behind those in the rest of England and in comparable English cities. So does the overall performance of London GPs against national targets, although there has been a marked improvement since 1990/91. While many aspects of provision and performance in general practice have improved in London, these have continued to improve in the rest of England as well. As a result, a substantial gap remains between the overall standard of services available for Londoners and those in the rest of the country.

There are also variations between different parts of the capital, with east London standing out as having poorer performance overall against targets, a more limited range of services available through general practice and a higher proportion of substandard premises and single-handed practitioners than other parts of the capital. General practice in south and south-east London performs better on most indicators than its counterparts north of the Thames (see Boxes 3.3–3.7).

Community health services

Community health services activity across London displays a higher degree of variation than is possible to explain in terms of response to need. Instead, analysis suggests that variations in performance are related to community health services providers rather than the characteristics of the populations they serve.

It is clear, however, that community nursing services in London are providing a higher intensity of care to London residents than their counterparts elsewhere in the country. On average, there are more district nurse contacts per individual patient in London. This is particularly true for inner-deprived London.

Local authority social services

As in 1989/90, local authorities spend significantly more per capita resident population on social services in London than is spent in the rest of England. Total social services spending is 60 per cent higher than the England average, and the London boroughs spend an average of 50 per cent more on older people as a group than is spent in the rest of the country. However, over the last five years, social services spending in London has increased proportionately less than in the rest of the country, at 37 per cent compared to 46 per cent.

As in 1989/90, the pattern of social services spending remains distinctively different in London, with proportionately more spent on domiciliary care than elsewhere in the country, and proportionately less on residential care. The London boroughs spend almost twice as much per capita on various forms of domiciliary care than their counterparts in the rest of England, and more than twice as much on day care. This reflects the higher cost of services in inner-deprived London as well as a higher volume of services provided per resident.

The London boroughs also spend more on residential care than their counterparts elsewhere in the country. Expenditure per capita on places for older people in residential care homes is 27 per cent greater than in the rest of England. This reflects the higher level of local authority-supported provision in inner-deprived London compared to the rest of the capital and its greater cost, as Figure 3.2 shows. The level of supported residential care for older people in mixed- and high-status areas of London is less than in comparable areas elsewhere in England.

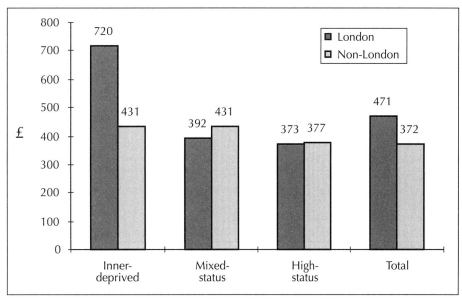

Source: Adapted from Boyle and Hamblin (1997)

Figure 3.2 Gross local authority expenditure on residential care for older people per capita resident population aged 75 years and over, London and England, 1994/95

Owing to the relatively limited availability of residential and nursing home care in many parts of the capital, London social services departments place people outside their boundaries more often than their counterparts elsewhere in England. Sixty per cent of nursing home placements supported by London local authorities are made outside their boundaries, compared to an average of 18 per cent in England as a whole. Many of these placements will be in other London boroughs, but a proportion will be outside Greater London.

There is marked variation in provision of nursing home places across the different sectors of London. East London has fewest at 9 per 1,000 population aged 75 and over, while in south London boroughs there are 38 compared to a rest of England figure of 51 per 1,000 population aged 75 and over. Within south London, certain local authorities have as many as 50 places per 1,000 population over 75. Inner-deprived London, however, has only one-fifth as many places relative to population as inner-deprived areas outside the capital. Local authority expenditure per capita on nursing home care is 13 per cent less than the England average (Boyle and Hamblin, 1997).

As in 1989/90, there remains a relative shortage of residential care places for older people within the capital. In London, there are 40 per cent fewer residential care admissions for older people when compared to the rest of England. This is particularly true for inner-deprived London, which at 30 admissions per 1,000 resident population aged over 75 has less than half the residential care admission rate of comparable areas of other English cities. These have an average of 69 admissions per 1,000 resident population aged over 75.

Hospital services

Hospital utilisation by Londoners

There have been pronounced changes in hospital utilisation by Londoners since 1989/90. When acute hospital care is considered – which excludes psychiatry, geriatrics and maternity – London had a higher acute hospitalisation rate, in terms of finished consultant episodes (FCEs) in 1989/90, than the England average – 133 FCEs per 1,000 resident population compared with 125. However, by 1994/95 the overall London rate was equivalent to the England average of 168.

In 1994/95 residents of inner-deprived London have a considerably lower hospitalisation rate than their counterparts elsewhere in England, with a standardised rate of 170 for inner-deprived London compared to a rate of 207 for other inner-deprived areas. In 1989/90 this difference was much smaller with a rate of 146 for Londoners compared with 148 for residents of inner-deprived areas outside the capital (Boyle and Smaje, 1992; Boyle and Hamblin, 1997).

Effectively, over the five-year period, acute hospitalisation rates have increased overall, reflecting increasing demand for health services, as well as increases in efficiency. However, in London, rates have increased more slowly than in the rest of England. There has been an equalisation of rates across London health authorities which has resulted in much less variation in hospitalisation between different types of socio-economic area in the capital than there was at the beginning of the 1990s.

Nationally, the increase in acute hospitalisation rates relates to an overall increase in day case procedures and to a rise in emergency admissions. Between 1990/91 and 1994/95 the number of emergency FCEs in England increased by 20 per cent compared with 19 per cent in London. However, the rates of increase in emergencies are extremely variable both between years, in-year and between different geographical areas and providers.

London as a whole has a lower psychiatric hospitalisation rate than the rest of England, primarily due to the extremely low rate in high-status areas, which is only 70 per cent of the England average. The psychiatric hospitalisation rate in inner-deprived London is 12 per cent higher than the England average. Inner-deprived areas of London also use substantially less geriatric care than similar areas in other parts of the country.

Hospital activity

There have also been marked changes in the composition of hospital activity since 1989/90. London continues to produce a higher percentage of hospital activity nationally than its percentage share of the England population. While 14 per cent of the population of England live in London, 16 per cent of hospital activity nationally takes place in the capital, when measured in FCEs. A greater proportion of London hospitals' workload is elective care (54 per cent), when compared to elsewhere in the country (51 per cent).

In 1989/90, the day case rate in London was similar to that for England at 19 per cent (Boyle and Smaje, 1992). By 1994/95, the proportion of total activity provided as day cases was higher in London (31 per cent) than elsewhere in the country (26 per cent). The difference for medicine is even greater: 30 per cent of episodes are day cases in London compared to 21 per cent in the rest of England (Boyle and Hamblin, 1997).

The higher day case rate in London relates to two factors: a higher proportion of elective cases than nationally and a higher day case rate among these elective cases. Day case rates vary across London. The north-west sector has a higher proportion of day cases than London as a whole in most specialties, with an overall rate of 36 per cent. Hospitals in inner-deprived London have a higher day case rate than their counterparts in other English cities. Sixty per cent of operative elective FCEs are performed as day cases in London. The rate varies from 57 per cent in the east and north-central sectors to 66 per cent in the south. This compares with a rate of just 53 per cent for the rest of England.

London hospitals continue to provide a considerable quantity of care to non-London residents. Overall, 14 per cent of acute activity at London hospitals is provided for non-residents. When account is taken of the use of hospitals outside the capital by Londoners, the 'net export' of acute care by London hospitals is 12 per cent, an increase of 2.5 percentage points from the position in 1989/90. Central London teaching hospitals and those close to the edge of London both 'export' approximately 15 per cent of their acute FCEs to the rest of the country. However, the inner-London teaching group exports care to all parts of the UK and abroad, while the 'border' group are used almost entirely by residents of the Home Counties on London's perimeter.

London hospital resources

The number of acute beds in London has continued to reduce. In 1995/96 it was 2.4 per 1,000 resident population compared to 2.9 in 1989/90. Bed availability has fallen less quickly in England, with the result that London in 1995/96 has just 5 per cent more acute beds per capita compared with the rest of England, a reduction from 15 per cent in 1989/90. When acute and geriatric beds are considered together, London has 3 per cent more than the average for the rest of England (see Figure 3.3). In 1995/96, including all beds in previous Special Health Authority hospitals, London has 22,000 acute and geriatric beds, some 5,600 fewer than in 1989/90.

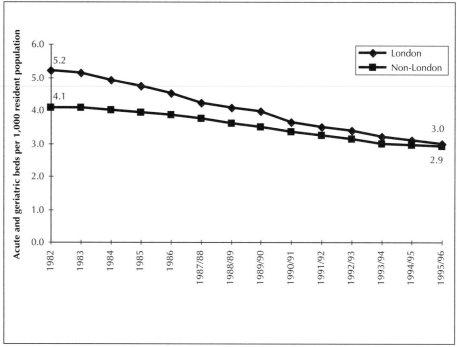

Source: Adapted from Boyle and Hamblin (1997)

Figure 3.3 Acute and geriatric bed availability, London and England, 1982 to 1995/96

Acute hospital beds are concentrated in the north-central and north-west sectors of London, as Figure 3.4 shows. More than half of London's trusts are located in these sectors, including almost all London's single-specialty hospitals and six out of eight former Special Health Authority hospitals. In contrast, the south sector has just 1.8 acute beds per 1,000 resident population, which is considerably less than the England average.

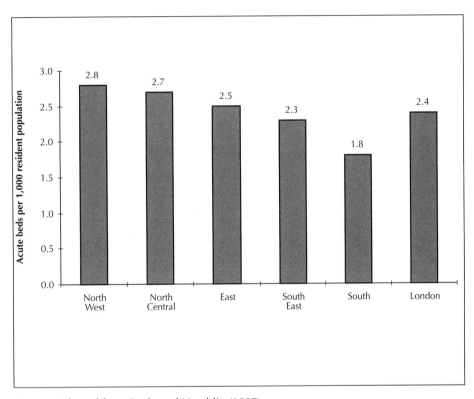

Source: Adapted from Boyle and Hamblin (1997)

Figure 3.4 Acute bed availability, by sector of London, 1995/96

In both London and England, there is a higher concentration of acute beds per capita resident population in inner-deprived areas than in other areas. In London, this reflects the location of 27 NHS trusts in the inner city. The rest of the capital – with a population two-and-a-half times greater than inner-deprived London – has only 38. As a result, inner-deprived London continues to have proportionately more acute beds than the rest of England, but there are fewer than average beds in mixed-status areas, as Figure 3.5 shows.

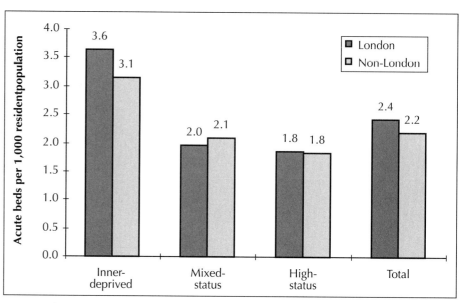

Source: Adapted from Boyle and Hamblin (1997)

Figure 3.5 Acute bed availability, London and England, 1995/96

However, just as 14 per cent of acute FCEs in London overall are provided to non-London residents, when hospitals in inner-deprived London are examined separately, 44 per cent of FCEs are provided to non-residents. A large proportion of these are residents of other parts of the capital.

As in 1989/90, hospitals in London have a distinctively different staff-mix when compared to the rest of England. Both acute and community trusts in the capital continue to employ more doctors and administrative and clerical staff as a proportion of total staff, and fewer nurses. This is particularly true of acute trusts in inner-deprived London, where, in some cases, the ratio of nurse to doctor is closer to three to one, compared to the national average of five to one.

Hospital efficiency

The substantial increase in the proportion of episodes in London hospitals treated as day cases was referred to previously. One consequence is that the average length of stay for acute inpatient episodes in London hospitals in 1994/95 shows a slight increase over 1989/90, from 5.6 to 5.7 days. The greater proportion of admissions treated as day cases probably results in an increased average complexity in inpatient cases.

An average length of stay of 5.7 days for acute inpatients in London is 16 per cent higher than the rest of England average of 4.9 days. On the other hand, a greater proportion of cases in London do not require an inpatient admission. Throughput, which measures the number of FCEs per available bed per year, is 76 FCEs in London as a whole, including day cases, virtually identical to the average of 75 FCEs for the rest of England. There is some variation across London, with a considerably greater throughput of 86 in the south. This reflects both a high day case rate and a low acute inpatient length of stay in that sector.

Rates of bed occupancy for combined acute and geriatric beds are higher in London than they are in the rest of England, at 86 compared to 79 per cent. Bed occupancy rates can be interpreted both as a measure of the efficient use of resources and as an indicator of pressure on scarce resources. A report by the inner London health authorities recommended that London hospitals maintain a bed occupancy rate of 85 per cent (Inner London Health Authorities, 1995).

BOX 3.3: HEALTH AND SOCIAL SERVICES IN NORTH-WEST LONDON

Primary and community health services

The quality of general medical services in the north west is similar to that of the rest of London. The proportion of premises below minimum standards and the proportion of practices without a practice nurse are relatively low, but the proportion of single-handed GPs and the proportion of GPs aged 65 years and over are slightly greater than the London average. There is a greater provision of community nurse contacts for mental health in this sector and rather less provision of speech therapy and chiropody. The north west has more community pharmacies relative to resident population than elsewhere in London, but these dispense fewer prescriptions on average.

Social services

There are far fewer residential care places for older people in the north west than elsewhere in London. This is reflected in the lowest admission rate to residential care in the capital. However, the level of residents supported by local authorities is close to the London average, implying that older people are placed in residential care homes outside north-west London.

Hospital services

This sector has the greatest concentration of teaching and specialist hospitals in the capital. This results in a greater availability of acute beds relative to resident population than in London as a whole. The unusual nature of hospitals in the sector is reflected in a unique pattern of activity. The north west has both the highest proportion of elective admissions and the greatest day case rate. Length of stay, turnover interval and inpatient throughput suggest that hospital beds are used less efficiently than elsewhere in the capital, but this is likely to reflect the more specialised activity in this sector. There is more private hospital care, both in NHS pay-beds and the independent sector in the north west than anywhere else in London.

The overall hospitalisation rate for residents of this sector is similar to that of London as a whole. Within this, the sector has a higher acute hospitalisation rate than elsewhere and a lower psychiatric rate. Residents make more use of private hospital care, whether in the NHS or the independent sector. Providers in the north-west sector receive a greater proportion of their income for education and research than elsewhere in the capital. Of income received for health services, a greater proportion comes from private patients than elsewhere in the capital. Income from GPFHs represents 5 per cent of services income, slightly greater than the London average.

Note: Trust configurations are indicated by two-way arrows between hospitals

Figure 3.6 Acute hospital trusts in the north-west sector of London

BOX 3.4: HEALTH AND SOCIAL SERVICES IN NORTH-CENTRAL LONDON*

Primary and community health services

Measures of general medical services quality and activity suggest that primary care in this sector is less well-developed than in the rest of London. In particular, the proportion of single-handed GPs and the proportion of premises below minimum standards are both greater than the London average. On the other hand, the proportion of practices without a nurse is similar to that of London as a whole. There are comparatively fewer GPs aged 65 years and over, and a greater proportion of GPs are on the minor surgery list. GP list inflation is twice the London average. There is a greater provision of specialist nurse and dietician contacts in this sector, but there is less than average provision of community nurses for learning disabilities.

Social services

There are more residential care places, particularly in the independent sector, in north-central London than in any other sector. Admission to residential care and local authority-supported residential home placements are close to the London average. With the exception of the proportion of households receiving home care, which is lower than elsewhere in the capital, the provision of non-residential social services equals the London average.

Hospital services

This sector has two teaching hospital trusts. It also has a large number of relatively small single-specialty hospitals. There are more acute beds relative to resident population than anywhere else in London. The prevalence of specialist hospitals is reflected in the relatively small number of staff at each trust. Patients in this sector are likely to be younger than those elsewhere: one in five admissions are aged under 15 years compared with one in seven in the rest of the capital. This sector has the highest attendance rate at A&E departments relative to local population, but the lowest average number of attendances per department. Private hospital care is significant, though less so than in the case of the north west. Independent hospitals in this sector attract a greater proportion of their workload from outside London than is the case elsewhere in the capital.

This sector has the greatest total hospitalisation rate of any sector of London. This is driven by a higher rate for geriatric specialties. The acute rate is close to the London average and the psychiatric rate is below. Trusts in this sector gain just 3 per cent of their health services income from GP fundholders.

*Maps showing the location of acute hospital trusts appear overleaf.

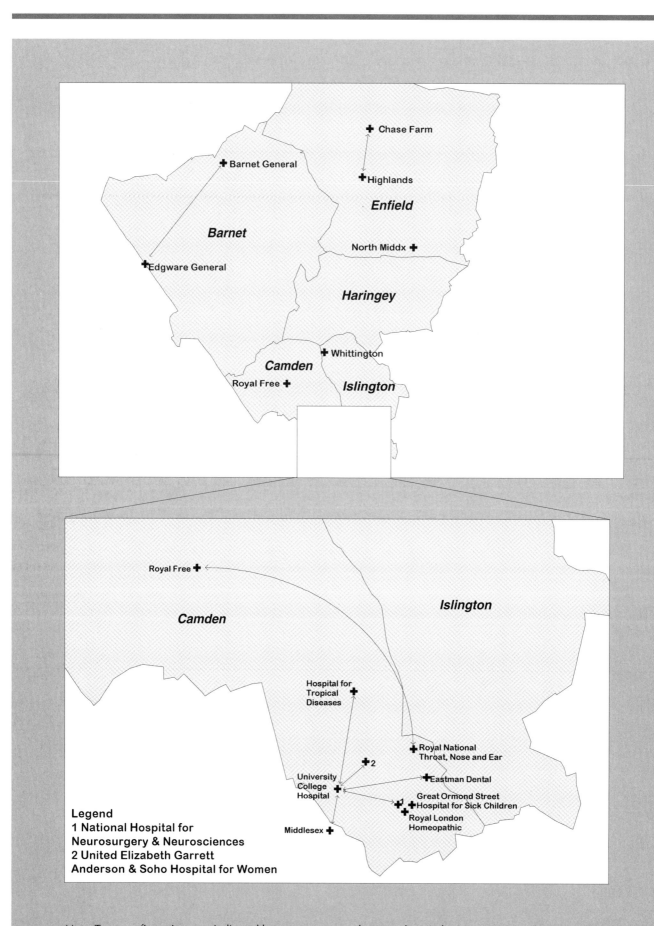

Legend
1 National Hospital for
Neurosurgery & Neurosciences
2 United Elizabeth Garrett
Anderson & Soho Hospital for Women

Note: Trust configurations are indicated by two-way arrows between hospitals

Figure 3.7 Acute hospital trusts in the north-central sector of London

BOX 3.5: HEALTH AND SOCIAL SERVICES IN EAST LONDON

Primary and community health services

There are more problems with general medical services in east London than anywhere else in the capital. This sector has the most premises below minimum standards, the fewest practices with practice nurses, the most single-handed GPs and the fewest GPs on the minor surgery list. Performance against activity targets is also low. The sector has the lowest compliance against immunisation and screening targets and the smallest proportion of children provided with health surveillance in the capital. There are high contact rates for community nurses for learning disabilities, specialist nurses and speech therapists.

Social services

Admissions to residential care for older people are at the London average, but only a quarter of these are to homes in the independent sector – the lowest proportion in the capital. In contrast, this sector has the highest rate in London of local authority-supported residents in residential homes for older people. The provision of non-residential social services is similar to the rest of London with the exception of home care, which is received by a greater proportion of households.

Hospital services

Local 'DGH-type' hospitals are more important in this sector than elsewhere in north London. There are five such

trusts, including two which combine acute and community services. There are less acute beds available than in other sectors north of the Thames. There is the highest proportion of emergency admissions in the capital, perhaps reflecting the deprivation of the local population and the paucity of primary care. Due to this high rate of emergencies, the day case rate is lower in the east than elsewhere in the capital. Although the population is younger, a greater proportion of finished consultant episodes are delivered to people aged 65 years and over than elsewhere in north London. Acute length of stay and turnover intervals are the lowest in London. This sector has the greatest non-attendance rate for outpatient appointments in the capital. Private hospital care is insignificant in the east. Private hospitalisation rates for DHAs, whether for NHS pay-beds or independent hospitals, are among the lowest in London.

The overall hospitalisation rate in this sector is close to the London average. The psychiatric rate is slightly lower than the average for the capital, but the geriatric rate is 10 per cent higher. Income not related to the direct provision of patient services accounts for 22 per cent of total income. However, providers in the east rely more heavily on DHA contracts as a source of services income than any other sector in the capital. GPFHs account for just 2 per cent of total services income.

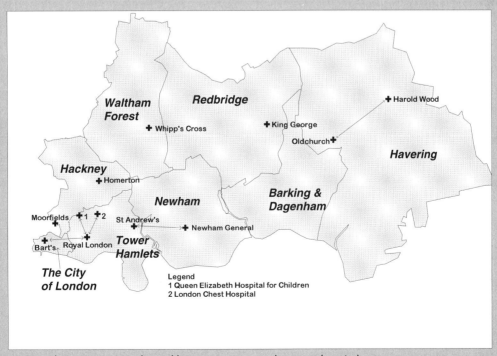

Note: Trust configurations are indicated by two-way arrows between hospitals

Figure 3.8 Acute hospital trusts in the east sector of London

BOX 3.6: HEALTH AND SOCIAL SERVICES IN SOUTH-EAST LONDON

Primary and community health services

More general medical services, and of a better quality, are provided in the south east than in any sector north of the Thames. The proportion of premises below minimum standards and the proportion of single-handed GPs are less than the London average. This sector has the smallest proportion of practices without a practice nurse in the capital, while the proportion of GPs aged 65 years and over is equal to the London average. The proportion of GPs on the minor surgery list is, with the south sector, the joint highest in London. Contact rates for both district nurses and health visitors are the highest in the capital. However, there are low contact rates for more specialist community health services such as community nurses for learning disabilities, specialist nurses and dieticians. It is possible that district nurses and health visitors in this sector fulfil more specialist roles.

Social services

The provision of residential care for older people in this sector is greater than elsewhere in the capital. However, local authorities support comparatively fewer residents relative to the rest of London. This sector has the highest provision of meals relative to population and there are more social services staff employed by local authorities than elsewhere in the capital.

Hospital services

This sector has two teaching hospital trusts, and one major specialist hospital. There are another four acute trusts. The availability of acute beds is slightly below the London average. Both teaching hospitals are large, and this contributes to the sector having the greatest number of NHS employees. The pattern of finished consultant episodes in the south-east is typical of London as a whole, whether disaggregated by specialty or by age-group. Overall length of stay is less in this sector than elsewhere, largely due to a low length of stay for non-acute specialties. Both throughput and turnover interval are unremarkable. Private hospital provision is not important in the sector.

The overall hospitalisation rate in the south east is the lowest in the capital. The three broad specialty groups – acute, geriatric and psychiatric – have hospitalisation rates below the London average; for acute and geriatric the rate is lower than any other sector. Services income represents a greater proportion of total income than in London as a whole. GPFHs account for 4 per cent of services income. The average cost per member of staff is less in the south-east sector than elsewhere in London.

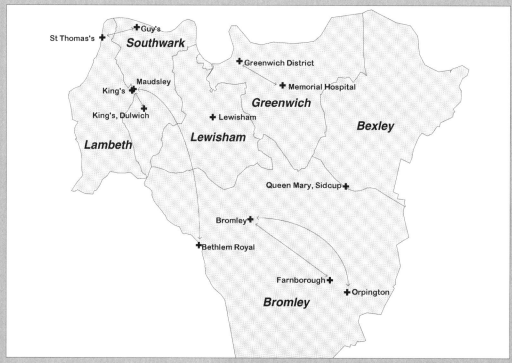

Note: Trust configurations are indicated by two-way arrows between hospitals

Figure 3.9 Acute hospital trusts in the south-east sector of London

BOX 3.7: HEALTH AND SOCIAL SERVICES IN SOUTH LONDON

Primary and community health services

The provision of general medical services, in terms of both quality and availability, is the best in London. A smaller proportion of premises are below minimum standards, a smaller proportion of GPs are single-handed, and a greater proportion of GPs are on the minor surgery list than in the rest of the capital. The proportion of children provided with health surveillance is the greatest in the capital. There are, however, more GPs aged 65 years and over than elsewhere, and the proportion of practices without a practice nurse is close to the London average. With the exception of chiropody, there are fewer community contacts relative to resident population than the London average.

Social services

This sector has a comparatively low level of local authority-supported residents of residential care homes. Residential care admissions for older people are close to the London average, but are less likely to be in the independent sector. By contrast, the proportion of meals provided by the independent sector is the greatest in the capital. However, the provision of meals is low, which may be counteracted by a higher attendance rate at day centres.

Hospital services

This sector has only one teaching hospital, itself unique in not being linked to a college of the University of London. There are no specialist trusts. The provision of acute beds relative to resident population is both the lowest in London and less than the average in the rest of the England. The proportion of elective admissions is less than the London average, but a greater proportion of these are day cases, resulting in a day case rate identical to the London average. There is some evidence that acute beds are used more efficiently than elsewhere: acute length of stay is low and throughput per bed is the highest in London when day cases are included. This efficient use of resources may compensate for the lower provision of acute beds. Neither the independent sector nor NHS pay-beds are particularly important in this sector.

The overall hospitalisation rate equals the London average. However, the psychiatric hospitalisation rate is the highest in the capital. Services income (87 per cent of total) is a more important element of total income for providers in this sector than anywhere else in the capital. This compares with 80 per cent in London as a whole. GPFHs account for 7 per cent of services income, the greatest proportion in London.

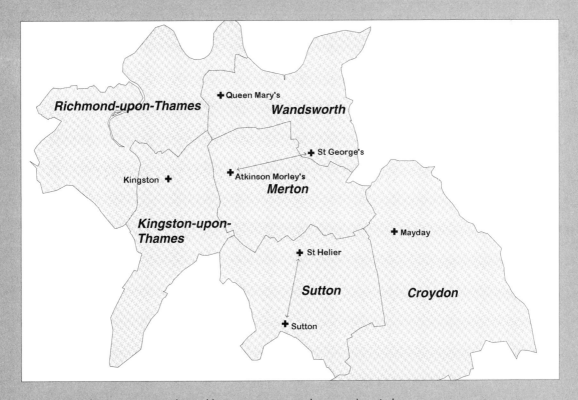

Note: Trust configurations are indicated by two-way arrows between hospitals

Figure 3.10 Acute hospital trusts in the south sector of London

Implications for the service system

Despite intensive development since 1993, it is clear from the evidence above that primary health care in London remains weak when compared with the rest of England and comparable parts of other English cities. Its performance also varies markedly across the city: general practice is relatively underdeveloped in the east and stronger in the south while the variability in performance of London's community trusts cannot be easily explained by differences in local needs.

The relative weakness of primary health care in London contrasts with the strikingly higher spending and provision on older people by social services departments in London. Lower social services spending on nursing home care and lower than average levels of geriatric provision in some parts of the capital certainly suggest that 'intermediate' or nursed care for older Londoners remains a gap in provision. It is also clear, however, that domiciliary care for older Londoners is more highly resourced and more widely provided than elsewhere in England, and may therefore compensate for this to some degree. As in 1989/90, expenditure on family health services remains comparatively low, especially when London Initiative Zone funding is excluded.

London hospitals have increased their efficiency since 1989/90. Their performance, particularly on day case work, has outstripped average performance elsewhere in England. Hospital utilisation by Londoners has increased as a result, as it has for residents in the rest of the country. However, the fact that the use of hospitals by residents of inner-deprived London has not increased at the same rate as that for comparable groups in other English cities gives grounds for concern. It is now on a par with that of residents of mixed- and high-status parts of the capital. This new pattern has emerged at the same time as hospitals in inner-deprived London have increased the proportion of elective care they provide for non-Londoners.

In itself, this development is surprising. It runs counter to predictions that London's hospitals would lose a proportion of their caseload, because their significantly greater costs would mean that their more distant purchasers would divert cases to less expensive local providers. The expectation was that the historic flows of patients into inner London would decrease, particularly for routine conditions (King's Fund, 1992; Tomlinson, 1992). This has not happened, although the cost of care in inner London remains the highest in the country. Instead, London's teaching and specialty hospitals have increased their market share of elective work to non-residents.

At the same time, the higher bed occupancy rates in London suggest that pressures on London hospitals may be greater than in the rest of the country, although the evidence on this is somewhat equivocal, since London hospitals also have higher than average lengths of stay. However, bed occupancy rates, and the very substantial move to day case procedures for elective work by providers in the capital, call into question the hospital system's ability to cope when there are greater than average numbers of emergency cases requiring admission. This is because the reduction in the beds required for elective cases means that there is an appreciably smaller 'buffer' bed stock available to be switched from elective to emergency work at times of peak demand – for example, during influenza epidemics or in periods of cold weather. The availability of beds in London has fallen to close to the national average. Together, these findings raise questions about the ability of hospitals to meet the needs of residents of inner-deprived parts of the city, particularly for emergency care and care of older people.

This complex picture of how London's health services are responding to the demanding agenda for change of the last five years is the outcome of interactions between the wide range of factors discussed earlier in this chapter. The next sections summarise this more generally – in terms of the overall system of health care in the capital – first by looking at some of the ways in which this system works badly, and second by identifying the strains that result.

System dysfunctions

Perverse incentives

While organisational arrangements for the NHS in London have been streamlined during the 1990s, this has been achieved at a price. The turbulence attendant on successive NHS and local authority reorganisations, along with the preoccupation with price-setting and the annual contracting round characteristic of the internal market, has diverted energy and resources away from the substantial service design and development tasks central to achieving positive changes to London's health care system.

Moreover, the establishment of trusts, as independent 'cost centres' with their own boards, financial regimes and performance targets has strengthened institutional loyalties and independence within London's hospitals. This has had benefits in terms of boosting efficiency and outputs, but co-operation between different parts of the service has been impaired. More worryingly, residents of inner-deprived London may be losing out as a result.

Collaboration on specialty rationalisation and the network of 'hub-and-spoke' hospitals advocated by the LIG specialty reviews was made more difficult because of the threat to individual institutions posed by the loss of a specialty. This threat has both clinical and financial components: the loss of certain key services – for example, accident and emergency departments, paediatrics or intensive care – potentially puts other specialties and/or training status at risk, while any decrease in activity means that fixed costs are spread over a smaller activity base, forcing trust prices to rise.

Effectively, the creation of trusts has reinforced the rivalry that has traditionally existed between London's hospitals. While in theory London purchasers can counter this by specifying the most appropriate patterns of care for their residents, service rationalisation poses risks to them in terms of higher prices from trusts. Given this, there is an in-built tendency for purchasers to protect local providers. This undermines effective collaboration between purchasers on services that span individual districts to cover large populations.

Absence of an overview

This problem is exacerbated by the absence of any body with the powers and capacity to take a London-wide view of the service system, and specialty provision within it (Harrison, 1997). Traditionally, this role was undertaken by regional health authorities, which controlled access to capital and had the expertise required to plan for specialties and super-specialties serving large groups. To do this, they drew on specialty advisory committees, through which clinical views could be accessed.

In London, this never worked perfectly since any city-wide overview was fragmented across the four Thames regions, but the system did have the capacity to link specialty planning with NHS revenue and capital allocations in a manner that could be informed by clinical leaders. These responsibilities have largely been devolved to individual health authorities or purchasing consortia. In the process, clinicians' perspectives have been side-lined, difficulties in accessing capital through the PFI have hampered action and any sense of overview has been lost in a welter of sectional interests. No clear view on how networks for specialty services would work in practice has emerged, although it is possible that the Department of Health's efforts to develop a national system of cancer centres and units providing appropriate programmes of care for individual patients may provide useful insights. The LIG model for specialty provision itself remains contentious: few trusts – or their clinical staff – see their future as being in a 'spoke' hospital only.

While the intention of the 1990 Act was to introduce greater flexibility into the provision of health and social care, it has been accompanied by a range of central initiatives that have limited the freedoms it offered. The purchaser efficiency index and NHS trust financial regimes are examples of these, as are waiting list, day case and Patient's Charter targets and a raft of central policy objectives, such as the introduction of the primary care-led NHS, and initiatives on emergency services and mental health.

While many of these are laudable in intent, they have complicated clinical and managerial agendas at a time of intense change. They have also introduced perversities: notably, the temptation for acute trusts to offload unmeasured work on other providers to improve their own efficiency. Overall, they have tended to focus managerial and professional attention on the parts rather than the whole (Harrison, 1997).

Diluted purchasing power in London

Perhaps as a result, health authority performance on needs assessment, service design and the development of alternative providers has been disappointing overall. A relatively small proportion of health authority resource is spent on needs assessment, and research conducted in London for the King's Fund London Commission suggests that, even so, a considerable proportion of needs assessment work undertaken within health authorities fails to influence the commissioning process (Millar, 1997a; Fulop and Hensher, 1997). In London, where commissioners have the most complex contracting portfolios in the country, a disproportionate amount of health authority time and effort is expended on the mechanics of contract setting, monitoring and financial control.

The role of health authorities in developing service strategies, design, specification and implementation remains relatively undeveloped. In any case, if they are to commission 'seamless' services for groups such as children, people with mental health problems and other adults with disabilities, skilled collaboration with NHS providers, commissioning GPs and GPFHs, local authority social services, housing, education and leisure, and local voluntary and user groups is needed. The multiplicity of interactions and complex boundary negotiations this involves in London makes this particularly daunting, as Chapters 4 and 5 explain further.

System strain

This analysis of health and social services activity in London highlights areas of major strain that are clearly visible within the system. These are multiple and tend to be mutually reinforcing.

Poor primary care

In many parts of the capital primary care performance and infrastructure remains distinctly below both the average for England and the position in comparable English cities.

Pressure on hospital services

Despite major increases in efficiency which have resulted in rising hospitalisation rates year on year, many trusts in the capital have not coped well with emergency admissions during the winters of 1995/96 and 1996/97. Trolley waits and precipitate discharges have resulted. The public perception that the NHS is unable to handle predictable seasonal pressures has contributed to the loss of public confidence in the London change programme discussed in Chapter 2 of this report. Waiting lists in London are now increasing, fuelling anxieties about access to care.

Difficulties with funding community care

In London, as elsewhere in the country, social services are having difficulty in resourcing care packages and residential and nursing home placements for people who need continuing social care. This has meant a tightening of eligibility criteria, increased emphasis on charging and delays in funding care, which have resulted in delayed discharges from NHS hospitals – something that has contributed to the pressures of recent winters discussed above.

Expensive care funded from constrained resources

Health care in London remains decidedly more expensive than in the rest of England, as Box 3.8 explains. Average cost per episode is over 20 per cent greater in London than in the rest of the country and varies by more than 50 per cent across the capital, from £760 per episode in the east sector to £1,190 in the north-west. The average cost per psychiatric episode in London is over 40 per cent more than in the rest of the country.

This reflects the higher cost of providing care in the capital in terms of staffing, land and premises. The distinctive pattern of medical staffing seen in London's hospitals contributes appreciably to London's higher costs and appears to have continued unaffected by the establishment of NHS trust financial and managerial systems. The average cost of staff relative to total FCEs delivered is considerably higher in London than in the rest of England. This is particularly true for medical staff: the cost of consultants is 40 per cent more per FCE in London than it is in the rest of the country.

During 1995/96, the financial position of NHS trusts in London deteriorated markedly, with 14 trusts operating a retained deficit – that is, a deficit after payment of interest owed and public dividend capital payments. The aggregated position of London's providers showed a £3 million retained deficit, in contrast

BOX 3.8: SPENDING ON HEALTH CARE IN LONDON

Family health services expenditure

As in 1990/91, per capita expenditure on family health services in London seems unexpectedly low when compared to the rest of England, given the higher costs associated with delivering equivalent services. Once again, London's position compared with the rest of England masks relatively higher expenditure on general medical services and lower spending on pharmaceuticals.

At £141 per capita, FHS expenditure in London is four per cent more than the average of £136 in the rest of the country. Average per capita expenditure varies between £130 in high-status areas of London and £158 in inner-deprived areas. However, LIZ funding accounts for £12 per capita in inner-deprived London. If this sum is subtracted, average per capita expenditure in inner-deprived London is just £3 more than in similar areas in the rest of the country. Expenditure on pharmaceutical services per capita is less and expenditure on GMS is more in the capital than in the rest of the country.

Hospital and community health services expenditure

As in 1990/91, the higher costs of care in the capital and the use of London's health services by non-residents mean that – at 19 per cent – a higher proportion of the NHS hospital and community health services budget is spent on health care in London than can be explained by either the proportion of HCHS activity in London (16 per cent) or London's percentage of the national population, which is 14 per cent of the England total.

Total DHA expenditure on HCHS per capita resident population varies from £423 in the south sector to £572 in north-central. Average DHA expenditure in London on HCHS per capita resident population is £483, over 30 per cent more than the average for the rest of England, which is £368. Inner-deprived London DHAs spend over 40 per cent more per capita than their counterparts in other English cities.

Costs-per-case remain significantly higher in London. The higher cost of care is partly explained by London's higher input costs. Staffing costs are higher and there is considerably more use of agency staff. The average cost per member of staff in London is £22,400 – 25 per cent more than the England figure of £17,900. The difference reflects higher wage costs in London, greater agency staff costs, and a greater proportion of more highly paid employees in London.

The average cost of staff relative to total FCEs delivered is considerably higher in London hospitals than in the rest of England. This is particularly true for medical staff: the cost of consultants is 40 per cent more per FCE in London compared with the rest of the country. The cost of non-consultant medical staff is 58 per cent more.

to the rest of England, where providers remained in overall surplus – albeit one that showed a sharp reduction on the previous year.

Six London trusts had retained deficits in seven figures in 1995/96. Following the tight public expenditure settlement for 1996/97, it is likely that when accounts for that year are published the situation of London's purchasers and providers will have deteriorated further. Twelve out of 16 London health authorities are over their capitation targets under the NHS funding allocation formula, and will therefore have received very limited growth monies in recent years. In fact, two London purchasers received emergency funding during 1996/97 to allow them to maintain basic services for their populations.

Skill shortages and workforce training issues

Skill shortages at a number of levels have deepened in London over the last five years. Shortages in psychiatry, paediatrics and accident and emergency services are a persistent feature of the capital, despite London's importance as a centre for medical education (Harrison, 1997). There are deep-seated problems of recruitment and retention in London's mental health services, with clinical and managerial staff reporting a high degree of 'burn-out' (Johnson *et al.*, 1997). London's GPs report dissatisfaction with increases in workload and spiralling public expectations, and younger GPs in particular are increasingly unhappy with traditional GP partnerships and working practices. This too is resulting in problems with recruitment and retention (Morley *et al.*, 1997).

At the same time, achieving productive teamwork within multi-professional, multi-agency community teams appears to be a problem in many fields, with mental health an area of particular anxiety, as the special study in Chapter 4 explains. It is not clear from this that health professionals and managers are being equipped with the skills they need to function well in today's health care environment, or being adequately supported in their day-to-day practice.

Conclusion

Five years into the London change programme, London's health care system is clearly under strain. Although there has been a considerable programme of investment within the London Initiative Zone, London's primary care performs poorly compared to other English cities. Despite marked improvements in efficiency, which have resulted in increases in hospitalisation rates overall, the internal market has encouraged London trusts to market elective procedures to non-residents. Londoners' access to hospital care may be suffering as a result.

Difficulties with staffing are entrenched. The cost of care remains high, and critical issues about patterns of medical staffing appear not to have been addressed by London trusts. Overall, the cost of health services in the capital is subject to an affordability gap which is posing an immediate financial problem to the service.

The 'Calman' changes to workforce deployment and medical education and postgraduate training demand changes in hospital organisation and working practices for which there has been little strategic planning. The organisational logic of this suggests amalgamation into larger units where specialised clinical teams can be more effectively deployed, but the politics of this have become much more difficult because of the perception of ordinary Londoners that service changes bring nothing but dis-benefits. Greater collaboration at specialty level across hospitals is another possibility, but it is not clear that London trusts, with their traditional rivalries, are well-equipped to work across organisational boundaries in this way.

These changes, and the related drive for increased specialisation in medicine, are introducing new costs into the hospital system at a time of severe resource constraint. In the longer term, the 'Culyer' changes to the funding of NHS research and development are likely to have a destabilising effect on London hospitals.

These strains are additional to the more general rise in expectations and pressures from technological change discussed in the first part of this chapter. They demand a modernisation and interlinking of health care systems which London seems poorly equipped to achieve.

The two chapters which follow summarise key messages from the special studies undertaken for the King's Fund London Commission on mental health and older people. Both of these centre on the capacity of the capital's health and social care systems to meet the needs of some of London's most vulnerable citizens.

CHAPTER 4

Mental health in London

Introduction

Chapter 1 has stressed the high levels of mental illness in London. These extremes are concentrated in inner-deprived London: outer London is similar to other suburban parts of England.

The intensity of mental ill-health in inner-deprived London results from a combination of factors. The first is poverty. Unemployment, social and cultural isolation, and poor living conditions foster vulnerability to mental illness. In inner London, substance abuse, homelessness and AIDS exacerbate the stresses created by deprivation and result in unusually high levels of mental ill-health. Refugees, a group with particular vulnerability to mental illness, also concentrate in London.

In addition, the high proportion of young people in London's population means a greater incidence of psychoses, substance abuse and personality and eating disorders at the point at which these conditions require the greatest intensity of interventions from health and social services. People with long-term mental health problems also tend to concentrate in poor inner-city areas close to transport hubs, such as railway stations.

The concentration of single-person households and people from minority ethnic backgrounds in inner-deprived London increases the demand for services. Distressed individuals who live alone require more help from statutory services. Minority ethnic groups require culturally appropriate services, and some experience increased incidence of mental health problems.

These factors combine to create exceptionally high levels of demand for mental health services in inner London. This, and the diversity of needs in the inner city pose particular challenges for service delivery.

Policy perspectives

Mental health services have been the subject of intense policy attention over the past decade. This has been fuelled by a series of 26 inquiry reports on homicides and other serious untoward incidents involving people with serious mental illness which took place between 1988 and 1996.

Nowhere has this scrutiny been closer than London, where 11 of these incidents took place (Johnson *et al.*, 1997). The Ritchie report on the case of Christopher Clunis had perhaps the greatest impact (Ritchie *et al.*, 1994). It called for improvement in care planning and inter-agency working, for advocacy services, for a greater range of residential care, for better assessment and recording of risk, for more culturally sensitive services and for highly intensive care to be available 24 hours a day. These recommendations have been reiterated in a number of other reports of independent inquiries, as Box 4.1 shows.

Some £10 million of extra funding was made available for London services following the publication of the Ritchie report. Ministers asked that the Mental Health Task Force work with the 12 health authorities within the London Initiative Zone, and to report with recommendations. These included:

- Pressures on acute beds should be addressed, with a reduction in the out-of-district placements which were draining resources from local facilities. Solutions to this problem would involve commissioning more beds in some health authorities, but would also be likely to require bed management strategies and alternatives to admission, including accommodation with 24-hour skilled staffing. A better understanding was required of the causes of pressures on beds. Plans for closure of long-stay hospitals and reprovision should be reviewed to ensure that timetables were manageable.
- Further development of community-based support was required, including housing, social support, day time opportunities and outreach.
- Inter-agency collaboration between health service, social services and other key agencies should be improved.
- Services should become more responsive to the needs of members of minority ethnic groups.
- Some innovative services did seem to be highly successful in meeting local needs – examples identified included the TULIP team providing intensive community outreach and support in Haringey, St Mary's early intervention service, a work scheme in Greenwich, the Star Centre drop-in in Hounslow and the Forward Project, which provides residential care and psychotherapy services targeting black service users in Hammersmith. The ring-fenced Mental Illness Specific Grant (MISG) funding, available to all local authorities nationally for mental health service development since 1991, was put forward as a successful way of promoting such initiatives.
- Spending on mental health services varied very widely between authorities, in ways that could not always be readily explained in terms of variations in levels of need.

Box 4.1: Mental health inquiries

The following list is a synthesis of the most frequently recurring themes emerging from the general reports on mental health services and from five of the inquiries on homicides. The numbers in brackets indicate the number of separate reports in which they figure (maximum number = 10)

Adequacy and allocation of resources (9)
The inadequacy of, or the need to protect, numbers of residential care places in London (including hospital beds) is a common theme (8). Specific mention is made of short-stay admission beds (4), medium-secure provision (4), and the importance of maintaining a wide range of community-based residential services (4), with DoH guidance on levels of provision. Comment is also made on the inadequacy of numbers of community workers (2) and of provision of day care services (2). Allocation of resources is commented on, both between competing groups (e.g. children, older people) (1), between health and social care (1), between areas of high and low need (2) and for the targeting of most severely ill people (3); as is the need for bridging money or ring-fenced money as services move from a hospital to a community focus (2).

Poor communication between agencies (7)
Particularly between health and social services (5), and between mental health services and housing departments (3). A related theme to this is that of poor joint working (4) which is at all levels, from commissioning and strategy (2) to multi-disciplinary care delivery (3).

Problems with discharge from hospital (5)
This particularly relates to failure to follow Section 117 procedures, assess need, develop an aftercare plan and communicate this adequately to other agencies.

Poor assessment of risk of violence (6)
This emphasises particularly the need for better and more training in risk assessment (4) and the importance of disclosure of risk factors to those with a need to know.

Liaison with police and probation services (5)
This relates both to the involvement of police in receiving or providing information about people receiving care from mental health services (2) and the need for greater involvement of mental health care workers in diversion from custody services (3).

Confidentiality and professional ethics (4)
These are reported as barriers, particularly between health and social services (2), and between mental health services and the police (2).

Source: Johnson *et al.* (1997)

The Task Force agreed specific six-month action plans with each purchaser, and worked with them on implementation. A follow-up report after six months reviewed progress on these plans. This found that collaboration between health and local authorities had improved, there was better prioritisation of severe mental illness and increased availability of support in some areas, along with increases in the availability of ethnically sensitive services and some increases in bed numbers (Johnson *et al.*, 1997). The work of the Task Force overlapped with LIG's work to foster innovation in primary and community mental health services. LIG's Mental Health Reference Group began its work in 1993, and by 1995/96 LIZ monies were funding 81 mental health-related projects, at a cost of some £10 million. This funding is now coming to an end, and pressures on health authority budgets mean that many will fail to be supported by mainstream funds.

Nationally, the policy response to the inquiry reports has spurred an accelerating number of plans, guidance, process measures and performance targets designed to improve performance within mental health services. These include the care programme approach (Department of Health, 1990); the Reed report advocating that mentally disordered offenders receive care and treatment within the NHS rather than custodial care (Department of Health and Home Office, 1991); the 'ten-point plan' for developing successful and safe community care of discharged psychiatric patients (Department of Health, 1993b); the supervision register, which requires health authorities to ensure that provider units identify and give priority to patients at significant risk (NHS Executive, 1994a); further guidance on discharge (NHS Executive, 1994b); the *Mental Health Patient's Charter* (Department of Health, 1997); guidance requiring health authorities to commission 24-hour nursed care (NHS Executive, 1996); and *Developing Partnerships in Mental Health*, the then Secretary of State for Health's Green Paper on joint working between health and local authorities (Secretary of State for Health, 1997).

In this increasingly fraught policy climate, mental health services in London have continued to grapple with seemingly intractable service problems. To understand these better, the next sections of this chapter examine the needs of Londoners with mental health problems, and the services available to meet them.

Meeting mental health needs

People with mental health problems commonly identify six major areas in which they require help and support. These are:

- access to information about mental health and mental health services;
- help with ordinary living to cover accommodation, an income, nutrition and self-care;
- personal growth and development;
- crisis support;
- planning;
- treatment, care and support for mental distress (Johnson *et al.*, 1997).

Within each of these main categories, the needs of individuals vary greatly. To take the example of needs in crisis, a long-term service user with schizophrenia will clearly require very different support and care from a clinically depressed young Bangladeshi mother. Her needs will in turn contrast with those of a homeless substance abuser.

In addition, severe mental illness impairs insight and judgement. People with mental health problems may, because of the nature of their illness, have difficulty in articulating their difficulties or in organising their care. Problems of this kind are particularly acute for isolated individuals living alone with no social network or family support.

Service response in London

Gaps in service

Currently, there is no London borough that has a fully comprehensive range of appropriate service responses using the definition above, despite the very great variety of service provision and types available within the capital. Problems exist in a number of areas. These reinforce each other and combine with conspicuous gaps in the range of services to create extreme pressures on both the service and the staff who work within it. This applies particularly to acute psychiatric inpatient services in inner-deprived London.

The variable quality of primary care in London means that mental health services remain poorly developed within it, creating a substantial gap in service provision for Londoners. This is particularly true for inner London, where mental health needs are at the extreme end of the spectrum nationally. Poor quality primary care in east London, where concentrations of deprivation are particularly high, gives special cause for concern (Johnson *et al.*, 1997).

Delays in accessing treatment

Londoners in need of mental health services frequently experience unacceptable delays in accessing treatment. Admission to acute psychiatric treatment is frequently delayed by more than two or three hours in parts of London, with much longer waits in some places. The average (median) delay in accessing a psychiatric intensive care bed is 24 hours. Delays of six months or more are commonly reported for accessing supported residential care places.

Poor co-ordination and care planning

The co-ordination of specialist mental health services with housing and other community supports remains problematic. Although substantial progress has been made in establishing community mental health teams (CMHTs) as the principal vehicles for co-ordinating care, treatment and support into integrated care plans, in practice the functions that these teams undertake vary greatly between different parts of the city.

Given this, it is unlikely that all or even most of them are proving effective at working with people with serious mental health problems to devise and monitor care and treatment plans in a way that links appropriately with primary care, housing, education, leisure and income support. The persistent problems with discharge planning and follow-up reiterated in repeated inquiry reports give evidence of pervasive difficulties with CMHTs' organisation and management. These are compounded by the fact that most community services are confined to office hours during weekdays, leaving London's accident and emergency departments as the most frequently used facility for emergency mental health assessment at any time.

In any case, the patchiness of service provision and shortages of appropriately trained staff, such as CPNs and psychologists, across London seriously impedes effective care planning. The provision of work schemes and daytime and weekend activities varies in a manner that is difficult to relate to local need. Overall availability is poor. Twenty-four-hour community crisis and intensive home-support services are almost completely lacking in the capital.

Shortages of rehabilitation facilities and acute psychiatric beds

Further, the availability of medium- and long-term community rehabilitation facilities, and local accommodation with appropriately calibrated support, appears to be appreciably worse in London than in other parts of the country. This gap has been repeatedly identified as contributing to the extreme pressures on acute psychiatric inpatient beds in inner London, where bed occupancy rates are exceptionally and unacceptably high. This is because at any one time almost a third of acute beds are 'blocked' by people who could be discharged if the right kind of community rehabilitation and/or housing was available (Johnson *et al.*, 1997).

The overcrowded, highly aroused atmosphere within many of inner London's acute psychiatric wards, with their frequent assaults, sexual harassment and high proportions of detained patients, creates an actively anti-therapeutic environment which is unsuitable for effective treatment. Staff 'burn-out' and exceptional difficulties with recruitment and retention of mental health professionals in inner London are attributable in large part to this (Johnson *et al.*, 1997). So are the problems that members of minority ethnic groups and women express about the inability of current services to meet their special needs.

This leads to inequities and waste. Staff shortages and serious gaps in community provision mean that admission thresholds are higher in inner London than elsewhere in the country. The result is that many of the capital's acute wards effectively offer a 'psychosis-only' service which excludes people with equally serious diagnoses, such as clinical depression, who would be admitted to hospital in other parts of the country. Extremely high rates of extra-contractual referrals to costly medium-secure and specialist private sector services outside the capital have been a feature of London's mental health services throughout the 1990s. Diversion of funds in this manner reduces the resources available to support services within London.

There is growing evidence of serious mismatches between statutory mental health services and the needs of Londoners. This applies particularly to children and adolescents, people with severe mental health problems and to the capital's minority ethnic groups.

Children and adolescents

London's high levels of social deprivation, its large refugee population and high rates of substance abuse and of children 'looked after' by local authorities or on child protection registers all indicate high levels of need for child and adolescent mental health services.

Crime, substance abuse, depression and suicide among adolescents have increased nationwide, along with increased vulnerability of young people to psychosocial disorder. It is likely that increased family conflicts may explain some of this higher incidence, along with increases in relative deprivation and in unemployment.

Responsibility for children and adolescents with mental health problems is split between the NHS and local authority social services and education departments. Service co-ordination is therefore particularly difficult in London because of the multiplicity and complexity of its administrative boundaries. The introduction of the internal market in the NHS has created a new layer of complexity, and there is some evidence that services have become less coherent as a result. It is also not clear whether health commissioners have developed the skills necessary for the effective purchasing of this specialist, low volume service (Johnson *et al.*, 1997).

Londoners with serious mental health problems

Research evidence suggests that local services are struggling to identify appropriate ways to serve people of working age with severe and enduring mental health problems, and most particularly young men.

There is a new generation of young and middle-aged Londoners with serious mental illness who have never received care in long-stay psychiatric institutions. Though in need of long-term care and support, the hostels, group homes, congregate day services and work schemes developed for people resettled from the old asylums do not find favour with them. They seek more individualised approaches. These will often need to include special housing arrangements, such as supported tenancies. Due to the inadequacies and gaps in provision mentioned above, suitable care packages are difficult to organise, with the result that repeated short admissions to acute psychiatric beds necessarily become the pattern of care. Difficulties in accessing appropriate housing and ineffective care planning have particularly serious repercussions for this group of people.

A subset of this group are substance abusers. These people with 'dual diagnosis' are typically male, prone to violence and offending, and display a chaotic lifestyle. Some are homeless. Unsurprisingly, they are difficult for statutory services to treat, or even to keep in touch with. When contact is made, many are poorly motivated to change or to comply with treatment. The complexity and multiplicity of their needs mean that they require intensive service responses that are orchestrated across health, social services, housing, and the benefits and criminal justice systems. Failure to achieve this orchestration through conventional service approaches means that people with dual diagnosis perceive the help they are offered as rigid, inflexible and inappropriate, and often reject it.

There is good evidence that the helping styles and working methods characteristic of mainstream mental health services are relatively ineffective in meeting the needs of people with dual diagnosis. Traditional outpatient appointments, for example, are unlikely to be helpful. Developments that appear to be more helpful – notably 'assertive outreach' and new forms of community-based crisis support, linked to 24-hour intensive home care – are lacking throughout most of the capital.

Research and development into effective ways of reaching and helping people with dual diagnosis and mentally disordered offenders is therefore a real priority, as well as greater shared learning about successful interventions. This will require the active participation of service users to be useful. Many of the service developments and innovative schemes that have emerged have been in the voluntary sector, and these tend to be poorly integrated with mainstream provision (Johnson *et al.*, 1997).

Londoners from minority ethnic groups and refugees

Londoners from minority ethnic groups experience particular difficulty in accessing treatment and care that are helpful and culturally acceptable. Statutory services do not seem to be effective at detecting mental health problems across all minority ethnic groups, engaging individuals from those groups in treatment or in gaining the confidence of minority communities. The marked tendency for Black Caribbeans to reach psychiatric services via the criminal justice system or through compulsory admission is one manifestation of this.

Such findings raise major issues about the ability of mental health professionals to devise treatment and care strategies that are effective for people from different cultures, whose help-seeking behaviours and expectations may be very different from those of the majority community:

> *'The culture of ward and community environments must change so as to re-capture the purpose of caring for the distressed; nowhere is this disparity more detrimental to patients than when the patient's cultural norms differ from those of decision-makers and providers.'* (Johnson et al., 1997)

Traditional responses to ill-health among minority ethnic communities tend to emphasise the need to treat the 'whole person', rather than a particular disorder. Black groups comment adversely on the absence of a holistic approach to mental and physical health within statutory services, and the under-representation of minority communities within mental health professions and management, particularly at more senior levels. Refugees in London experience a set of related difficulties: especially vulnerable to depression, anxiety and suicide, they may often fail to find treatment and care that are relevant to their particular experiences and present circumstances.

Once again, the most effective response to these needs has come through the voluntary sector. In a number of parts of London, local community and religious groups have taken the lead in developing culturally appropriate mental health services for minority ethnic groups and for refugees. The services they provide include day care, home care and information services. Although they are often the only form of support accepted by minority ethnic communities, they are frequently poorly integrated with the statutory services. This, and their fragile funding and organisational base, mean that they are all too easily marginalised.

Comprehensive local services

To be comprehensive and effective, local services need to provide a range of care settings and treatment approaches. Supported housing; home support services capable of sustained 24-hour interventions, seven days a week; employment and activity schemes to cover daytimes and weekends; and crisis and treatment services, including acute inpatient and rehabilitation beds are all essential components of comprehensive local services. Each of these components should be capable of addressing the needs of people from minority ethnic groups. They must also link effectively with specialist services for mentally disordered offenders, and for children and adolescents.

Care planning has a central role in ensuring that support and treatment are designed to meet individual needs and preferences. If this is to work well, individuals with mental health problems and their families must actively participate in constructing care plans. High quality information about mental health and the treatment and support options available locally are therefore essential. So is access to local housing, including supported tenancies, income support and benefits advice, education and meaningful daytime, evening and weekend activities (Johnson *et al.*, 1997).

Pressure on mental health services in the 1990s

Failure to establish a comprehensive range of local services has created a number of pressure points on London's mental health services in the 1990s. The most visible of these is the over-occupancy of acute psychiatric beds. This is the clearest manifestation of a vicious circle fuelled by the absence of community rehabilitation, supported housing, day services, supported work schemes and the rest.

There are, however, submerged tensions and difficulties that mean that London's service system is particularly poorly equipped to address the substantial problems that confront it. These have surfaced repeatedly in the inquiries into untoward incidents that have characterised mental health services in the 1990s. They relate to funding levels and approaches to care.

Funding levels

Health and local authority spending on mental health services varies considerably between inner and outer London. There is also considerable variation in spending per capita across the capital, and this and related variations in levels of service provision are not easily reconciled with epidemiological and socio-demographic estimates of need. Instead, they are likely to relate to historic spending patterns – most particularly, whether the district concerned had had responsibility for a Victorian asylum (Audit Commission, 1994).

Inner-London purchasers spend a greater part of their budgets on mental health services than their counterparts in other English cities. However, current pressures on health and social services budgets are very likely to divert resources away from mental health in many London authorities, thus exacerbating a situation of serious strain. Difficulties in accessing capital for service developments such as acute psychiatric or rehabilitation facilities under the Private Finance Initiative appear to be even more intractable than for other acute services (Meara, 1997).

Inner-deprived London continues to suffer from its historic lack of local mental health provision, and further investments to alleviate extreme service pressures are required. The 1970s and 1980s saw the transfer of psychiatric services into inner London from the peripheral asylums, in many cases for the first time. The scale of underprovision in the 1990s suggests that service developments undertaken then are insufficient, and the shortfall is made more acute by the fact that growing unemployment, inequality and deprivation in inner London are generating increasing mental distress.

At present, it is difficult to see a way forward for mental health services in the capital without the resources to support a sustained programme of service development. Resource allocation formulae nationally need to be altered to reflect the special intensity of mental health needs in the inner city. If Londoners' needs are to be met, however, these resources should include those available through local information, housing, benefits advice and employment services. 'More of the same' in terms of a narrow focus on expanding the range of services traditionally available within NHS and local authority statutory mental health services will be wholly insufficient to meet the scale of the shortfall. There is a need to shift the paradigm within which mental health services operate and reframe it in terms of the full range of resources available to support citizens within local communities.

Systemic problems with inter-agency and multi-disciplinary working

Disagreement about what constitutes mental health, mental illness and effective approaches to treatment leads to conflicts between professional groups within mental health services. Practitioners within mental health services can have divergent theories and views of the nature of mental disorder, and these differences contribute to the tensions of joint working at agency and at team level.

This is manifested in the communication difficulties and conflicts about leadership, respective roles and effective management that have dogged the development of CMHTs in London and elsewhere. Problems with teamworking within community-based services surface repeatedly. The degree of dysfunction evident within multi-disciplinary teams of this kind suggests that they may best be viewed as transitional arrangements, from which more coherent methods of assessment, care management and treatment should be actively encouraged to emerge.

It may be that these entrenched problems can only be addressed over the longer term, through multi-disciplinary training and education strategies. In any case, national shortages of psychiatrists, psychologists and community psychiatric nurses – by which London is particularly badly affected – suggest that a sustained programme of workforce planning based on the requirements of a community-based service is overdue.

Tensions between health and social services

Statutory responsibility – and state funding – for mental health services is divided between health and local authorities. The different cultures and accountability structures of the NHS and local government are well documented and contribute to long-standing difficulties with effective working of community care policies locally (see, for example, Audit Commission, 1986).

These were entrenched well before the 1990 Act, but the implementation of the community care legislation in 1993 has heightened tensions between the NHS and local government. Both have been confronted with tightening resources and the need to define eligibility for services. Despite exhortations from central government, real and perceived attempts to shunt costs between agencies locally mean that it has often proved difficult for these criteria to be defined collaboratively. The result is that individuals fall through the net.

In mental health, as in other areas of community care, this situation has undermined the trust which is essential for successful joint working and cross-agency service development at local level. It also contributes to the difficulties of cross-agency working experienced by many of the capital's CMHTs. All in all, it encourages a climate of defensiveness in which creative problem-solving aimed at addressing local service deficiencies jointly is unlikely to flourish.

The multiplicity of institutional boundaries in London, coupled with the number of London boroughs and the fact that few health and local authorities in the capital are coterminous, creates particular obstacles for joint working. In some parts of London, these problems are beginning to be compounded by new cross-agency tensions engendered through local responses to developing a primary care-led NHS.

This is an area where collaborative service development is urgently required. It is difficult to engage social services in designing mental health service responses which support GP practices effectively without the active support and involvement of senior local authority officers and local politicians. Where this is not forthcoming, new barriers to joint working will result.

Tensions between primary and secondary mental health care

Within the NHS, the intensity of the current policy focus on people with severe and enduring mental health problems has created tensions between primary and secondary care, particularly in the context of policies designed to foster a primary care-led NHS.

General practitioners, whose practice lists typically include substantial numbers of people with disabling depression, anxiety and phobias, frequently have difficulties with what they perceive to be the unduly restricted remit of secondary care. At the same time, they can feel ill-prepared to care for people with severe mental illness. Their specialist colleagues fear that demands from GPs will divert limited resources from people with severe mental illness – who largely have psychotic disorders – to less disabled groups.

These tensions – which are growing as GP fundholding and other forms of GP commissioning strengthen in London – need to be addressed through collaboration on priorities and joint working which also involves social services. If this fails to happen, the commissioning of mental health services will become hopelessly fragmented. Such a collaboration would be facilitated by a broadening of national policy on mental health to reflect more adequately the legitimate perspectives of primary care practitioners and of people with mental health problems themselves.

Service fragmentation

Implementation of the community care legislation has required social services departments to commission increasing amounts of care from voluntary and private sector providers. This, and the use of joint finance and NHS funding for similar purposes, has meant that the independent sector is playing an increasingly important part in London's service system.

In many places this has introduced refreshing new approaches to service delivery. However, in many parts of the capital, independent sector services remain poorly integrated. Poor communication and co-ordination are the result, with an inevitable negative impact on the care and support individuals and families experience. This is most evident in services for older people, but also applies to minority ethnic groups, homeless people, and people with 'dual diagnosis', as discussed above (Johnson *et al.*, 1997).

At the same time, housing, leisure and education services remain poorly connected to mental health services. Changes to housing legislation, in particular, have increased the difficulty of accessing supported and other forms of housing for which people with serious mental illness would previously have been given priority. This has compounded the difficulty of supporting people with long-term mental illness who have never been institutionalised.

Effective interventions and treatments

User groups' involvement in service planning and the new emphasis on evidence-based practice within the NHS are raising questions about the effectiveness of conventional helping strategies, treatments and professional practice within mental health services. The manifest difficulty of designing and accessing appropriate services for people from minority ethnic groups and for people who have never been institutionalised, as discussed above, emphasises the importance of service development. This must be supported by research and evaluation that have as their goal improving outcomes for service users through the application of evidence-based practice. Users and their families need to participate directly in this.

The issues apply more widely, however: the effective design and use of secure services and of services that meet the particular needs of women are examples where work on effective practice and new forms of service delivery is required, to be following by service development, evaluation and dissemination. The scale and complexity of this service development challenge are underplayed within current national mental health policy, with its emphasis on a (seemingly) set 'spectrum of care'.

Workforce shortages and 'burn-out'

Shortages of psychiatrists, psychologists, community psychiatric nurses and approved social workers are apparent nationwide, and the problem is particularly acute in inner London, where the pressures on staff are intense. Staff 'burn-out' – that is, low morale, high rates of sickness absence and high turnover – and resulting difficulties with recruitment and retention are now a conspicuous feature of services in inner London. Staff's reported sense of being poorly supported in a service which is under intense public scrutiny clearly contributes to this problem (Peck *et al.*, 1997).

Managerial instability

Recent research into the factors contributing to successful joint working highlights the importance of long-term relationships, stability of personnel in key positions, shared agendas, priorities and values and the ability to access joint funds to achieve shared goals. These factors are particularly important in London, where organisational boundaries are complex. However, mental health service managers in London – many of whom have clinical backgrounds – have experienced multiple organisational restructuring and many changes of role following the implementation of the NHS and Community Care Act 1990. The instability and organisational turbulence this creates reduces the ability of services to adapt appropriately to the many challenges they face. The fact that relatively few mental health service managers have specific management training also limits capacity for change within the system.

Central policy initiatives

These tensions have not been allayed by the plethora of policy initiatives on mental health from the Department of Health during the 1990s. These have tended to concentrate on process – the care programme approach; the supervision register – and focus on the NHS. Increasing policy prescription from the centre has resulted in muddle at local level. The duplication and confusion attendant on the introduction of care management within social services and the care programme approach in the NHS give the best evidence of this.

The end result has been clinical and managerial focus on processes and individual service elements, rather than on the service system and the outcomes it delivers for service users and their families. The host of 'challenge funds' and 'target funds' has created a prize money culture which has reinforced this fragmented approach. All this has contributed to a widespread perception that mental health services are 'overtasked and undermanaged' (Johnson *et al.*, 1997).

At the same time as central policy has imposed processes designed to ensure that people with serious mental health problems are effectively supported, supervised and treated in the community – for example, the supervision register – changes in housing legislation have made it more difficult for local authorities to prioritise people with serious mental health problems. Central policy has so far failed to address barriers to effective joint working, such as the inability of health and local authorities to pool budgets to achieve shared service objectives and separate performance management and accountability systems, although this might change if certain of the options put forward in the Green Paper, *Developing Partnerships in Mental Health*, are adopted (Secretary of State for

Health, 1997). Overall, national policy for mental health services has concentrated on the 'what' of service development at the expense of the 'how'.

Conclusion

London's mental health services are operating in a manner that is clearly unsustainable. The situation described above cannot continue without unacceptable risks to service users, their families and other carers and intolerable strain on staff.

Recommendations

A number of recommendations for change are suggested by this analysis. They include the following:

1. Public health approaches to London's mental health

- Mental health services development should be reframed within a wider, more inclusive approach to mental health within national and city-wide policies. This 'paradigm shift' should include action at national level to promote mental health, and reduce the social and environmental stresses that contribute to mental illness. This might include the application of a 'mental health test' by government to policies originating from the Department of the Environment, the Department of Social Security and the Department for Education and Employment to establish their impact on factors implicated in mental illness.

- Within London, community and borough development and regeneration programmes need consciously to include measures to support the mental health of Londoners, with a particular accent on the mental health of young people. If the shift is to be successful, an approach to mental health that involves the full range of community interests and resources locally is needed.

2. Local mental health plans

- Development of joint commissioning approaches between health and local authority social services and housing departments is an urgent priority in London and elsewhere. This should be facilitated by moves by central government to encourage the pooling of NHS and local authority allocations for local mental health services, and the development of appropriate accountability mechanisms. To avoid further confusion and alienation within the service, any changes should be designed to minimise structural disruptions.

- Health authorities and local government should be required to produce costed and timetabled local mental health plans jointly. These should cover community development and other initiatives designed to promote mental health. Local service developments should be identified collaboratively between health and local authorities and local providers, with full user and community involvement, to include the voluntary and private sectors.

- Plans should be based around the functions that services deliver for the people they serve, rather than on service 'models'. They should include appropriately phased investments in new or additional service elements, which should be firmly linked to financial and business plans. Standards for access to treatment should be set within the plans, and closely monitored.

- Health and local authorities' progress in achieving the goals identified in local plans should be jointly monitored by the NHS Exccutive and the Social Services Inspectorate. Evaluation and monitoring should be based on outcomes achieved for service users and their carers. Effective, acceptable services for people from minority ethnic groups should be a particular priority.

- NHS trusts should be encouraged to provide 'social' care, to be funded from local authority allocations, in order to encourage more coherent service provision.

- Practical care planning processes should be devised with the explicit purpose of connecting the planning of health and social care for individuals with the realities of the whole of their lives, to include housing and employment.

3. Resource allocation

- Allocation formulae should over time be adjusted to ensure equity based on socio-demographic and epidemiological factors. As this takes place, it will be important to ensure that the special needs of deprived inner cities, and the particular needs of inner London, are adequately reflected within allocations.

- Any additional allocations for mental health should be made to rectify service gaps and deficiencies identified within local mental health plans (see above) rather than in response to one-off 'bidding' processes.

4. Improved information and monitoring

- Major improvements in current information and monitoring systems are required. These should be better standardised across providers to ensure that meaningful comparisons can be made between them and across authorities and statutory and voluntary sector providers.

- As investments are made and services developed there should be a conscious effort to assess their impact on the system as a whole. Audit, evaluation, computer modelling techniques and simulations may prove helpful here, along with development of integrated care pathways designed around users' needs and experiences.

5. Human resources

- Exploration, review and debate of professional roles and accountabilities within community mental health services should take place, preferably at the instigation of the professions themselves, but with full participation of service users and other stakeholder groups. The outcomes should be explicitly designed to inform future professional and managerial practice – for example, job plans and multi-disciplinary teamworking – and education and training. Wherever possible, professional education and training should be joint to foster mutual understanding and appropriate patterns of working.

- Urgent work needs to be undertaken on ways of attracting and retaining mental health professionals to work in London. This should include an appreciation of appropriate ways of supporting staff in their work in the inner city.

- Concerted attempts to improve the cultural competence of mental health services across London are required. These should include appropriate training and recruitment strategies.

6. New knowledge

- Evaluation of the effectiveness of intensive 24-hour community services to prevent admission or reduce the length of stay within psychiatric inpatient provision should be commissioned.

- Research on effective helping strategies and treatments for people from minority ethnic communities should be commissioned, in partnership with representatives from those communities.

CHAPTER 5

Older people in London

Introduction

Good housing, an adequate income, worthwhile ways of spending the day, personal safety and good health all contribute to living well in later life. Like other Londoners, older people are dependent on the whole life of the city for their well-being. Like other Londoners they are a diverse group, displaying greater extremes of wealth and poverty and a more cosmopolitan mix of culture and ethnicity than in any other part of the United Kingdom.

The health of London's older people

As Chapter 1 has stated, London has a relatively low share of older people, and their number is predicted to decrease. This decline is likely to continue until the middle of the next decade. However, the age structure of London's older population is unusually weighted towards the oldest age-groups, so that the average ages of both older men and older women are greater than the rest of England. The number in advanced old age has increased markedly during the 1990s, but this trend is abating, and decreases are predicted as the century turns. London already has the highest concentration of people from minority ethnic groups in late middle and old age of any part of the United Kingdom. It is projected to experience the largest absolute increases of older people from minority ethnic groups in the country (Warnes, 1997).

London's distinctive age structure is partly created by the migration of older people out of the city at retirement and at later ages. Patterns at any given age are complex and include a proportion of people with illnesses and disabilities moving outside the city for nursing home care or to be closer to relatives. In general, however, people approaching and passing through the age of retirement in London have a very high rate of departure. This exodus is selective of owner-occupiers, middle- and higher-income groups and the white population. Its net effect is to lower the average socio-economic status of those who remain (Warnes, 1997).

London has the highest proportion of older people living alone of any part of the United Kingdom. In addition, the exceptional mobility of London's population means that family networks are more dispersed, and there is a low prevalence of care by relatives. The average distance of an older person to their nearest child is high by national standards.

Housing standards for older Londoners are marginally worse than in England as a whole, but better than in other cities. Renting remains relatively common in London. Apartments and sub-divided accommodation with poor amenities and access can create problems for older people living in poorer parts of the city.

The health of older Londoners is generally better than that of older people in the rest of England. The majority of people aged between 60 and 80 are fit and well. Utilisation of formal health services increases steadily in all age-groups from late middle age. Older people in their late 60s and early 70s experience increased cardiovascular disorders, orthopaedic problems and cancers and therefore have relatively high needs for health services when compared to younger people. Slower recovery from illness and interventions is also a common characteristic. A few diseases have a strongly rising prevalence through the oldest ages, such as the dementias and osteoporosis. Within any of the older age-groups, however, people with complex multiple health problems and high levels of disability and dependency are a minority, even well into the ninth decade of life.

Compared to other parts of England, Londoners experience a substantially lower incidence of deaths at all ages within a number of disease categories. This is true for cardiovascular diseases and cancers (Benzeval et al., 1992). However, detailed work on mortality rates from stroke suggests that although standardised mortality ratios for this condition in London are lower than the national average, this overall picture masks high rates of stroke that are related to deprivation and ethnicity, particularly in the youngest pensionable age-groups. Such findings reflect the fact that Black-Caribbean populations, in particular, have an 8–9 per cent higher incidence of stroke than the overall population. Findings of this kind underline the fact that as the ethnic composition of London's older population changes, health needs and health status within the capital will alter to reflect the specific needs of minority ethnic groups (Warnes, 1997).

Utilisation of health and social services

Most older people require the same sort of health care as younger people do. Treatment can generally improve health and functioning in older people. Recovery from episodes of ill-health tends to be normal. However, the long-term and recurrent nature of many of the health problems characteristic of later life means that older people require greater co-ordination between organisations and individuals that provide care.

When asked about their concerns with statutory health and social services, older Londoners, like their counterparts elsewhere, raise a consistent set of issues:

- poverty, expressed particularly about the level of the basic pension;
- affordable, accessible transport;
- information about available services;
- independence in the home;
- safety and security;
- discharge from hospital (London Health Partnership, 1997).

Overall, it is extremely difficult to track the use made of the health and social care system by older Londoners. There are numerous gaps and inadequacies with current information sources, and the data they provide are not consistent or readily comparable. This reflects the fragmented nature of the services available to older people – of which more below. There is also a conspicuous absence of information from older people themselves, their families and other carers about their experience of the service system and the outcomes it achieves for them. As a result, it is impossible to obtain an adequate 'system-wide' perspective of the services available to older people across the city (Warnes, 1997).

The picture that does emerge has a number of similarities with the mental health study in the previous chapter. This is one of service fragmentation and notable variability of service provision across the capital. Both raise worrying questions about older Londoners' access to care.

Primary and community health services

As Chapter 3 makes clear, the performance of general practice in London continues to lag behind both national standards and that in comparable English cities. This long-standing pattern has particularly serious implications for older Londoners, who rely on GPs and the wider primary health care team for continuity of care. There is little evidence on which to assess the treatment provided to older people specifically by GPs. Survey data suggest greater use of GPs among people aged between 65 and 74 years in London as a whole when compared with the rest of England. The same is true of women aged 75 years and over, but not of men. In the same survey this is balanced by lower usage of inpatient hospital services (Warnes, 1997).

Community health services face particular difficulties in London. They must liaise with many more acute trusts and social services departments than their counterparts in the rest of the country. As a result, good communication, smooth handovers between providers and continuity of care for individual patients – all of which are particularly important in communities with relatively high numbers of older people living alone – are markedly more difficult to achieve.

The evidence on community health services suggests considerable variation in the availability of services in the capital. The use of district nurses and health visitors is approximately equivalent to that elsewhere. However, London residents make more intensive use of services than those elsewhere, suggesting possibly higher levels of need or dependency. Some community trusts report rapid increases in their case-loads during the first half of the 1990s and an increase in the intensity of the care their patients require. This may relate to the surge in the number of very old people within London over the same period, as discussed earlier. This is also suggested by evidence collected from special surveys in one area of London which suggests both that there has been an increase in overall provision in the last five years, and that there has been a substantial increase in provision to people aged 85 years and over, who are identified by the report as those most in need (Warnes, 1997).

Social services

In London, as in the rest of the country, the implementation of the 1993 community care provisions of the NHS and Community Care Act 1990 is uneven. Fewer needs assessments for community care have been completed than are required, and the rate of completion varies considerably across the boroughs (Warnes, 1997).

A distinctive feature of social services provision for older residents of London is its bias towards care in people's homes rather than residential care. Table 5.1 compares the provision of domiciliary and residential care between London as a whole and the rest of England.

Table 5.1 Residential and domiciliary care for older people, 1994/95

	Inner-deprived London	London	England
Per 1,000 population aged 75 and over			
Residential care places	48	49	75
Nursing care places	11	19	47
Meals	509	405	232
Per 1,000 population aged 65 and over			
Day care centre attendances per week	43	34	19
Households receiving home care	101	71	57

Source: Adapted from Boyle and Hamblin (1997)

As Chapter 3 has stated, there is substantially greater provision of all forms of community-based care per capita resident population in London when compared to the rest of England. Most of this day care and home care is used by older people. However, levels of provision vary across the capital (Boyle and Hamblin, 1997).

In London overall, local authorities support a similar number of people per capita resident population aged 75 and over in residential and nursing homes as are supported in the rest of England. However, the substantially lower rates of provision of residential and nursing home places within the city mean that older Londoners often have to move outside their borough of residence to receive this type of care. For many, moves of this kind will further attenuate family and friendship ties.

This is particularly true for residents of inner-deprived London, where levels of local provision are the lowest in the country. However, inner-deprived London local authorities support a greater number of older people in residential care than their counterparts elsewhere at 40 compared with 32 per 1,000 resident population aged 75 or more (Boyle and Hamblin, 1997).

Across the full range of social services provision, over 50 per cent more is spent by London local authorities on care of older people per head of older population than in the rest of England.

Hospital services

There is considerable variation in the use of hospital services by older London residents. Although, for each five-year age-group over the age of 60 years, older Londoners as a whole have a higher hospitalisation rate than their counterparts in the rest of England, the position in inner-deprived areas of the capital is very different. There is a lower hospitalisation rate at each five-year age-band, for both men and women. Differences range from over 20 per cent less for women aged 75 to 79 years to 10 per cent less for men of a similar age.

Table 5.2 shows the numbers of finished consultant episodes (FCEs) per 1,000 resident population by sex for those aged 65 or more. For all five-year age-groups above 65 years hospitalisation rates are exceptionally low, with the shortfalls for some groups exceeding 15 per cent. There are considerably fewer FCEs relative to the resident population of inner-deprived London when compared to similar areas elsewhere in England. However, high- and mixed-status areas of London have higher per capita FCE rates than comparable areas outside, which means that overall hospitalisation rates for older people in London are above national levels. Figures 5.1 and 5.2 illustrate this for men and women aged 65 and over.

Table 5.2. FCEs per 1,000 resident population by five-year age-group aged 65+, 1994/95

	Age-group (years)	Inner-deprived		London as % of non-London	Total		London as % of non-London
		London	Non-London		London	Non-London	
Male	65–69	378	424	89	374	344	109
	70–74	453	521	87	453	425	107
	75–79	575	636	90	560	531	105
	80–84	641	746	86	647	626	103
	85+	725	825	88	743	716	104
	65+	489	552	89	492	461	107
Female	65–69	271	308	88	267	248	108
	70–74	310	363	85	306	297	103
	75–79	370	447	83	373	371	101
	80–84	447	528	85	454	451	101
	85+	557	604	92	541	509	106
	65+	369	422	87	368	352	105

Source: Warnes (1997)

Box 5.1 compares hospital utilisation by older Londoners for two of the most common diagnoses, cataracts and acute myocardial infarction. Differences in utilisation rates are striking both between inner-deprived London and comparable areas elsewhere and within the capital. These findings clearly merit further investigation, since they raise questions about the access that older people in inner-deprived parts of the city have to hospital treatment.

This pattern of lower utilisation by older inner-deprived Londoners is accentuated when the number of hospital bed days occupied by older people in 1994/95 is considered. Figure 5.5 shows considerably lower rates for all age-groups. This striking difference in the use of beds by older people from similarly deprived areas reflects the fact that older Londoners have shorter lengths of hospital stay and more day case treatment than their counterparts elsewhere.

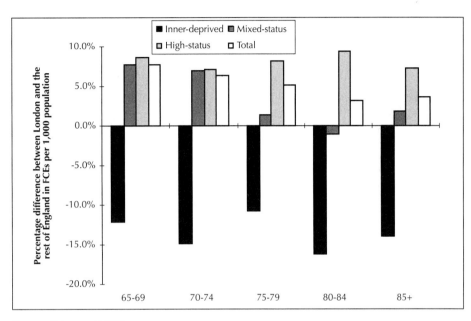

Source: Warnes (1997)

Figure 5.1 The percentage difference between London and England in FCEs per 1,000 resident population, males aged 65 years and over, 1994/95

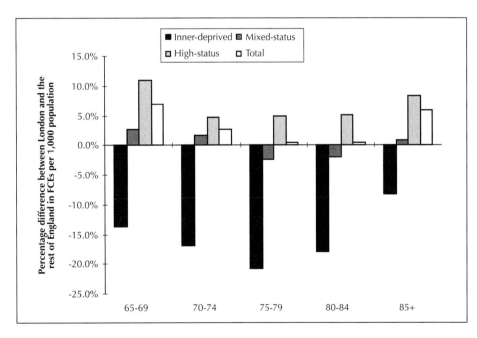

Source: Warnes (1997)

Figure 5.2 The percentage difference between London and England in FCEs per 1,000 resident population, females aged 65 years and over, 1994/95

BOX 5.1: HOSPITALISATION RATES FOR OLDER PEOPLE IN LONDON

FOR TWO COMMON DIAGNOSES

Two of the most common diagnoses among people aged 65 years and over in London are cataracts and acute myocardial infarction. The first of these, cataracts, generally requires an elective admission. Figure 5.3 shows differences across age-groups and by sex. The female rate is between 30 and 40 per cent greater than that of the older male population, in London and England. However, significant differences are revealed when inner-deprived Londoners are compared with their counterparts elsewhere. For most age-groups and both sexes, the rate in inner-deprived London is less. However, it may be significant that an exception occurs in the younger cohorts. Males and females aged between 65 and 69 years have higher rates than the same age-group in the rest of the country. The extent to which earlier treatment compensates for the differential in later rates requires further detailed examination.

		Inner-deprived		Total	
		London	*Non-London*	*London*	*Non-London*
Female	65+	189	212	204	191
Male	65+	151	164	160	139

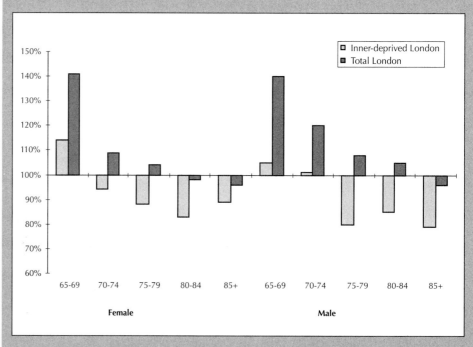

Source: Warnes (1997)

Figure 5.3 Cataract FCEs per 10,000 resident population in London as a percentage of comparable England figures, for people aged 65 years and over, by sex and five-year age-groups, 1994/95

Acute myocardial infarction tends to occur as an emergency. Figure 5.4 shows, for inner-deprived older Londoners, hospitalisation rates for most five-year age-groups and both sexes are considerably below those in comparable areas in the rest of England. Differential access may be a factor here, although there is evidence suggesting that Londoners have lower mortality rates from this specific cause.

		Inner-deprived		Total	
		London	Non-London	London	Non-London
Female	65+	56	102	61	69
Male	65+	89	156	109	119

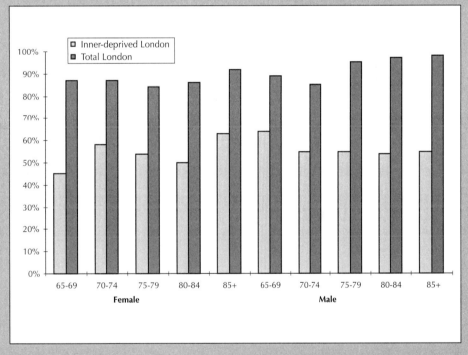

Source: Warnes (1997)

Figure 5.4 Acute myocardial infarction FCEs per 10,000 resident population in London as a percentage of comparable England figures, for people aged 65 years and over, by sex and five-year age-groups, 1994/95

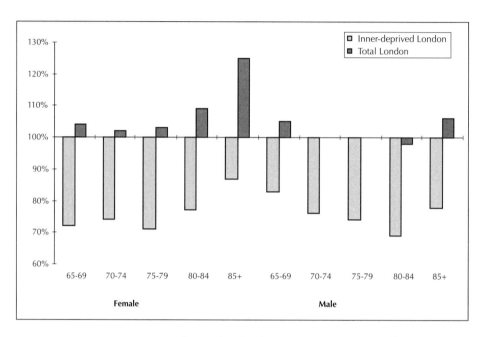

		Inner-deprived		Total	
		London	Non-London	London	Non-London
Female	65+	5,301	6,694	4,995	4,400
Male	65+	4,953	6,430	4,416	4,286

Source: Warnes (1997)

Figure 5.5 Annual occupied bed days per 1,000 resident population in London as a percentage of comparable England figures, for people aged 65 years and over, by sex and five-year age-groups, 1994/95

'Care of the elderly', or geriatric, services are unevenly provided across London. In 1994/95, 5 per cent of total London hospital activity was in the geriatric specialty – virtually the same as the national average. There were marked local variations, with the geriatrics share being 20 per cent greater in the north-central sector but 16 per cent less in north-west London (Boyle and Hamblin, 1997). There are also marked differences between socio-economic areas of the city, with less geriatric medicine capacity within the inner-deprived London hospitals. Psychogeriatric bed availability is similarly variable across the capital (Warnes, 1997).

The 'care of the elderly' specialty addresses the needs of older people with multiple chronic conditions. The goal of geriatric medicine is to maximise patients' physical functioning, independence, emotional well-being and self-esteem. This 'holistic' approach is reflected in the specialty's tendency to work in multi-disciplinary teams, which frequently have a community orientation. The relative underdevelopment of the specialty in London may mean that older Londoners with multiple chronic conditions experience less well-integrated care than their counterparts in other English cities.

Overall, this evidence suggests that older residents of inner-deprived London have poorer access to hospital care than their counterparts in other comparable English cities. It could be argued that older Londoners have lower levels of need, or that lower use of hospitals is a good rather than a bad thing. However, when matched against other evidence on the relative needs of the population and poor access to primary care, access to hospital services is an issue which merits further investigation.

The health and social care system for older people

Box 5.2, which is based on a recent report by the Health Advisory Service, gives an indication of the complexity of arrangements for the commissioning and provision of health and social care for older people nationally. Effectively, the system is highly fragmented, with an absence of oversight or of a strategic perspective (Health Advisory Service, 1997).

The Health Advisory Service examined multi-disciplinary assessment of older people and the delivery of continuing care across the country. It found that despite the good intentions of commissioners and providers, 'older people with complex needs are falling through the cracks between agencies. Services are fragmented, there are problems with funding, a lack of proper assessment and reassessment, inequity, and inadequate communication' (Millar, 1997b). The report's overall view is that while services 'are by no means in a parlous state', the purchaser-provider split has created 'perverse incentives and unwelcome boundaries to communication and to the seamless delivery of care'. Among the more serious obstacles, it argues, is GP fundholding which has 'fragmented the purchasing role, dispersed the financial resources of health authorities and denuded them of personnel' (Health Advisory Service, 1997).

The Health Advisory Service encountered problems between health and social services agencies, mostly concerned with the funding of long-term and continuing care, which led to difficult relationships. It also found that, where separate hospital and community trusts provided a range of health care services for older people, they were not working to achieve seamlessness in the provision of care. Instead, an holistic, multi-disciplinary assessment at a number of different stages requires a process that, as far as possible, involves GPs and primary health care teams, 'care of the elderly' team specialists, social workers, health visitors, care managers and informal carers. This demands rigorous and inspired collaboration between these different elements (Warnes, 1997). The case for this applies particularly strongly in London, where more older people live alone and/or without effective informal care.

BOX 5.2: SERVICES FOR OLDER PEOPLE

Health services for elderly people are commissioned by health authorities and purchased by:

- health authorities;
- GP fundholders.

Both of these processes are augmented in parts of England and Wales by locality purchasing teams, and by non-fundholder consortia.

Health services for elderly people are provided by:

- primary health care teams;
- acute hospital trusts;
- some trusts that provide centres for the referral assessment, and management of people who require very specialised care (e.g. for orthopaedic, neurosurgery and cardiac surgical services);
- community-based trusts;
- trusts that provide mental health services.

Social care for elderly people is commissioned and purchased by:

- social services departments (purchaser/assessment team care managers);
- elderly people themselves;
- carers and the relatives of elderly people.

Social care for elderly people is provided by:

- social services departments (provider units);
- voluntary sector agencies;
- the independent sector;
- people (usually relatives) who care for older people (informal carers) or who support these carers.

The role of 'informal' carers is the largest of these, although the contribution they are currently permitted to make to the formulation of policy is often minimal.

Although the social services departments have the lead responsibility for ensuring the provision of social care, these services are also purchased by private or charitably funded non-statutory agencies, health authorities and GP fundholders. In such a system, there is a high likelihood of local difficulties arising in agreeing a uniform strategy, as well as delivering services at an operational level to users with complex needs.

Source: Health Advisory Service (1997)

Commissioning care for older people

In London as elsewhere, responsibility for commissioning the care of older people is dispersed across a number of agencies. At the purchasing level, health authorities and local authorities share an ill-defined set of responsibilities, often with neither funded adequately to meet these in full.

This leads naturally to an effective failure of leadership for service development. This is especially true for the identification of needs of older people. Evaluating needs which are difficult to satisfy is attractive to neither statutory agency (Challis and Pearson, 1996). Moreover, recent years have seen an increase in efforts to shift responsibility for funding across agency boundaries. This relates to the changes to community care funding made in 1993 as part of the implementation of the NHS and Community Care Act 1990.

Under the 1990 Act, care assessments, the design of care packages and purchasing became the responsibility of social service departments. At the same time, their role as direct providers of residential and domiciliary care was to be reduced. In practice, there have been long delays in undertaking assessments and funding care packages, creating problems with the discharge of patients for acute trusts.

London's shortfall of private sector residential and nursing home places creates additional problems, particularly in inner London. In this service area, the capital's existing institutional complexity has been heightened by the markedly different policies of adjacent boroughs in inner London – a complication faced by no other English city. Some boroughs have been keen to encourage the privatisation of domiciliary and residential care, while others have been reluctant to do so. The result is that a further dimension of variability has been added to London's existing patchwork of provision.

The community care plans produced for 1995/96 and/or 1996/97 by all but three of the London boroughs' social service departments were analysed for the King's Fund London Commission, as well as 36 annual reports, business plans and primary care plans from within the NHS in London (Challis and Pearson, 1996). This analysis identified a number of serious problems with needs assessment and service development that undermine the effectiveness of the commissioning process. These include:

- a general inability to find relevant population data for planning purposes and to translate the information into demand projections for different types of services;
- an unwillingness or inability to break away from present service configurations to enable innovation in service organisation and delivery;

- an incapacity to handle and reconcile data from different agencies or with different definitions and structures, and for the most part insufficient data skills to design the simplest counts of inter-sectoral flows;
- problems between the boroughs in adopting consistent approaches to the identification and quantification of need – in many places information from individual needs assessments rarely appears to influence agency-level planning;
- the absence of any mechanism for encouraging consistent or comparable methods and procedures through all London boroughs;
- local authority 'takeovers' of planning processes – such as community care plans – which need to involve close partnership with the NHS to be effective.

The picture that emerges is one of an absence of vision or strategic direction for services for older people within the capital. Neither health nor local authorities separately hold an adequate overview, and effective joint working often falls victim to the very real financial pressures that both statutory agencies experience. Given these general problems, it is unlikely that the special diversity of older Londoners' needs are being adequately addressed.

Approaches to health and social care provision

Responsibility for provision is even less clear. Most younger people's main contact with formal health services is with their GP. They occasionally require hospital treatment. They are unlikely to come into contact with services for which local authorities are responsible unless they have mental health problems or a physical or learning disability.

However, older people often need higher rates of treatment and care from formal health services, and their needs increase with age. They require continuity of care over time and across organisational and agency boundaries. Older people with complex needs – and their families – frequently find it difficult to see where ultimate responsibility for their care lies, or to define where it should rest. Is it with the GP, with the social worker, district nurse, home carer or with the hospital consultant's team? Given current arrangements, none of these is able to provide adequate cover and co-ordination to support a full and healthy life for older people.

These are general problems faced throughout the United Kingdom. However, the multiplicity of administrative boundaries within London means that the situation within the capital is considerably more complex. London has 32 local authorities plus the City of London, each with its own social services department. There are 68 NHS trusts in the capital. The majority of them deal with residents of more than one local authority, particularly those that deliver acute health care. The situation for acute and specialist hospitals in inner-deprived London is particularly extreme, since many of them deal with substantial flows of patients across whole sectors of London and the rest of the South East.

Given the administrative complexity generated by this degree of cross-boundary working, it is especially difficult to maintain adequate services for older people in London. Essentially, the complexity of co-ordination and liaison between organisations and teams of professionals is too great for effective integration in many parts of the capital. Service co-ordination and continuity of care for individuals – both of which are especially important for older people – therefore pose a challenge which is in practice unachievable under present arrangements.

Solutions must address the needs of older people so as to allow them to live a safe, healthy existence. This involves more than health and social service provision on their own: availability of transport, sufficiency of income, social contact and personal safety are all important. Nevertheless, the system of health and social care in London can address three key issues.

- First, clear accountability for older people's services must be developed. By understanding needs better it will be possible to design system-wide solutions for individuals and communities which address future as well as current or immediate problems.

- Second, financial allocations to statutory bodies need to be consistent, to reflect their differing responsibilities adequately. Disincentives to integrated care should be eliminated.

- Third, through central strategic management and local organisations working together across provider boundaries, it should be possible to ensure that information systems are put in place which permit effective monitoring.

Conclusion

Health and social care is only one of many contributions to full and active lives for older people. Good living conditions, an adequate income, personal safety and worthwhile ways of spending the day are all important.

However, in terms of improving health and social care for those who need it, integration of care to meet individual needs is the critical issue for older people – particularly for the minority that have complex, multiple conditions. This cannot be achieved through the present system, where responsibility for commissioning health and social care is split between two different statutory agencies and responsibility for delivering care across widely disparate constellations of provision. The issues are more difficult in London where administrative boundaries are the most complex in the country. The clear leadership required is currently lacking.

Overall, it is clear that the health and social services available offer older Londoners a poor deal. Given their high costs, this also means that they represent poor value for money.

Recommendations

1. Public health policies for older people in London

- The health and social care of older people should be recast within a wider, more inclusive approach to the well-being of older people within national and city-wide policies. This will require greatly improved policy co-ordination for social security and environmental policies as well as health and social care.

- Within London, community and borough development and regeneration programmes need consciously to include measures to support the well-being of older Londoners, including their safety. If this approach is to be successful, it must encompass the full range of community interests and resources.

2. Local plans for older people's services

- Development of joint commissioning approaches between health and local authority social services and housing departments is an urgent priority in London. This needs to be facilitated through moves by central government to encourage the pooling of NHS and local authority expenditures on local services, and the development of appropriate accountability mechanisms.

- Health and local government should be required to produce costed and timetabled local plans for the development of older people's services. These should cover community development and other initiatives designed to promote the well-being of older people.

- These plans should be based around the functions and outcomes that services deliver for older people, rather than on service 'models'. The aim here, as elsewhere, is to organise care around individuals' requirements.

- Plans should involve appropriately phased investments in new or additional service elements, which should be firmly linked to financial and business plans. Standards for access to treatment should be set within the plans and closely monitored.

- Local access to hospital and 'intermediate' care, to include nursing and residential home provision, needs to be a particular focus of these local plans.

3. Resource allocation

- Allocation formulae should be adjusted over time to ensure equity based on socio-demographic and epidemiological factors. It may well be, for example, that formulae should become more sensitive to the proportions of the very old, and the very old living alone, within the older population.

4. Human resources

- Education, training and recruitment policies designed to encourage culturally competent services for older people should be put in place.

5. Improved information and monitoring

- Major improvements in current information and monitoring systems are required to permit care to be better integrated around the needs of individual older people.

- Information should be better standardised across providers to ensure that meaningful comparisons can be made between them.

- As investments are made and services developed, there should be a conscious effort to assess their impact on the system as a whole. Audit, evaluation, computer modelling techniques and simulations may prove helpful here, along with the development of integrated care pathways designed around older people's needs and experiences.

CHAPTER 6

A new policy framework for health services development in London

Forces for change: the challenges restated

In the UK and internationally, health and social care systems are experiencing pressures for change that make inherited patterns of services and institutions unstable, as Chapter 3 to this report makes clear. Key issues which have emerged are:

- health is recognised as the proper focus for health policies – health services and their supporting structures need to be understood as one important means of improving or maintaining health;
- a combination of increased public expectations, quality improvement initiatives and changes in demography and technology is challenging traditional forms of health care provision;
- national policy requirements for medical education and training are having a profound impact on the way in which specialty services are organised, both within individual hospitals and across them.

The complexity of the interconnections among these pressures and uncertainty about the effect of new treatment technologies make precise predictions about their eventual impact difficult (Harrison, 1997). However, there is new thinking about the shape of services locally. Within acute health services, there is greater specialisation and concentration in certain specialties at the same time as technological changes assist the dispersal of others to more local settings. Both tendencies have led to a renewed emphasis on primary care as a focus for care co-ordination and continuity in addition to its traditional roles of assessment, diagnosis, referral and treatment.

Overall, there is an emerging emphasis on health care and social support integrated around the needs of individuals. This relates to a recognition of the need to improve the service response to people with conditions such as cancer or long-term mental health problems where co-ordination and continuity of care are critical.

All these influences highlight the need for strong connections between provider organisations, for changed professional roles and for heightened teamworking. This implies related changes to professional education and clinical research and development.

These pressures and trends have particular resonance for London as the home of 7 million people and as a major health services, education and research centre. Chapter 2 of this report makes clear that the need for significant change to the capital's health services, medical education and research has been a recurrent subject for health policy attention throughout this century. However, progress has been painfully slow, reflecting the complexity of the issues and the strength of the sectional interests involved.

In the early 1990s, the first King's Fund London Commission and Tomlinson concluded that the balance within London's health service system was wrong and would be strained to breaking point by the introduction of the internal market. Both recommended major investment in London's primary care and the restructuring of hospital services, medical education and research in the capital. The London change programme that resulted attempted to accelerate the modernisation of health services in the capital by a three-pronged effort to:

- significantly improve primary, community and continuing care;
- rationalise the provision of acute services and specialties across institutions and sites to ensure a better distribution of services, improved efficiency, improved quality and the release of resources for community-based services;
- provide the conditions for better medical education and health services research linked to major academic centres.

For this agenda to deliver substantial improvements in the health and health care available to Londoners, the institutional changes described in Chapter 2 need to be understood as only a first step – and one that is by no means a guaranteed stepping stone – to improvements in health services, medical education, and research. It is through these and – ultimately – through improvements to the health of Londoners that success should properly be judged.

The London context

While change on this scale would be challenging anywhere, Chapter 3 of this report and the Commission's special studies on mental health and older people described in Chapters 4 and 5 highlight some of the reasons why achieving success in London is particularly difficult. These include:

- the size, complexity and diversity of the city and its people, which are greater than any other European capital;
- the complexity of its administrative boundaries with the fragmentation of local government across 32 boroughs and the City of London, which greatly complicates the delivery of effective community care;
- the parochialism that can result from the very strength of London's institutions, many of which have long and distinguished histories;
- the potentially destructive competitiveness consequent upon proximity among many similar providers;
- the likelihood of conflicts being magnified by closeness to Westminster and the national media.

The change agenda

Although the London change agenda still makes sense in broad terms, five years into implementation, progress has been erratic and often slow. Improvements in primary care infrastructure and in service innovation have occurred, although these last have all too often failed to be funded long-term.

Chapters 1 to 5 reveal that in a number of significant respects London's health care system has not developed over the last five years in ways which meet the needs of Londoners. Key problems are listed in Box 6.1.

Overall, London's health and social services still appear to offer Londoners a poor deal, despite the fact that they are more costly than equivalent services in other English cities. The London Commission's special studies suggest that services for people with mental health problems and older people are fragmented, provider-dominated and relatively unresponsive to the needs of individuals and families, although they cost more than their counterparts in other English cities.

There has also been a failure to convince Londoners of the need for changes to their health care system. Well-publicised problems during recent winters, long waits in accident and emergency departments and rising waiting lists for planned surgery have heightened Londoners' anxieties about the ability of the NHS to provide adequate care. These have not been effectively countered by the investments in primary care infrastructure and services, which have been markedly less visible. As a result, many Londoners and some groups of NHS staff are alienated from the change programme and disillusioned with NHS planning processes.

Box 6.1: Key problems for health services in London

- There is no comprehensive programme to tackle London's health inequalities. The 'Health of the Nation' programme in the capital – as elsewhere – concentrates on clinical 'targets' and does not sufficiently address the social and economic determinants of health. Health promotion and health services development within the NHS tend to be divorced from the wider urban regeneration agenda across the capital, particularly where community development initiatives and/or investment in health care infrastructure is involved.

- General practice in London still lags behind that in other parts of England, and equivalent parts of other English cities, despite substantial investment.

- Inner-London trusts have heightened their efficiency, and increased productivity has resulted in an increase in the elective surgery available to non-residents. However, in the process, hospitalisation rates for local people have fallen well below those of comparative areas outside the capital. The implications of this for the health of Londoners is worrying. In particular, the ability of older people living in inner-deprived parts of the capital to access appropriate care and treatment is called into question.

- There is a pressing financial problem in London, both with purchaser budgets and with the ability of trusts to continue to meet financial targets. Two London purchasers received emergency funding during 1996/97 to allow them to maintain services for their populations. Twelve out of 16 London health authorities are over their capitation targets under the NHS funding allocation formula. Currently, a higher than average number of London trusts are failing to reach their targets, and a number are being supported through 'transitional relief' from central funding.

- Although plans to reconfigure acute hospital services have caused enormous controversy and hostility in many parts of the capital, implementation has stalled because of delays in agreeing capital funding for redevelopment under the Private Finance Initiative (PFI). This, and opposition from sectional interests, have stymied the rationalisation of specialties.

- Acute bed numbers have fallen to close to the average for England, but sites have not closed. In consequence, fixed costs are spread over a smaller service base. This contributes to even higher costs in London. Furthermore, capital has not been released for re-investment.

- Spreading a smaller number of beds across the same number of hospitals, combined with the reduced number of elective beds due to the switch to day case surgery, also reduces flexibility to deal with peaks in emergency admissions. In practice, the capital's acute hospital services have not coped well with emergency admissions during the winters of 1995/96 and 1996/97. These very public failures sap public confidence in the NHS and fuel resistance to change in the capital.

- If, as on present evidence seems likely, the PFI fails to deliver the schemes required to reduce the overall revenue costs of London's hospital services, the hospital system is likely to consume a greater proportion of resources and may even prove financially unviable in the longer term (Meara, 1997). Moreover, PFI delays have slowed the reconfiguration and consolidation of medical teaching and research, where very substantial positive progress has been made.

- Skill shortages at a number of levels have deepened in London over the last five years. Shortages in psychiatry, paediatrics and accident and emergency services are a persistent feature of the capital, despite London's importance as a centre for medical education. There are deep-seated problems of recruitment and retention in London's mental health services, with clinical and managerial staff reporting a high degree of 'burn-out' along with a perception that they need to be better supported for the work they are expected to carry out (Johnson *et al.*, 1997).

- At the same time, achieving productive teamwork within multi-professional, multi-agency community teams is a persistent problem in many fields – with mental health being a particular worry (Johnson *et al.*, 1997). Health professionals and managers are not being equipped with the skills they need to function well in today's health care environment.

- London's GPs report dissatisfaction with increases in workload and spiralling public expectations, and younger GPs in particular are increasingly unhappy with traditional partnerships and working practices. This too is resulting in problems with recruitment and retention (Morley *et al.*, 1997).

- Despite continued expressions of concern at policy level over the better part of a decade, mental health services are under severe strain, and nowhere in the capital is a comprehensive range of services on offer for Londoners.

- The complexity of administrative boundaries between the NHS and local government in London and the inability to pool budgets between them create formidable obstacles to effective service development.

- People from London's many minority ethnic groups find that services are poor at responding to the needs and preferences of their cultures and communities (Johnson *et al.*, 1997).

- There are difficulties co-ordinating care for older people. These are manifested in failure at the interfaces between forms of care: hospital and home; between types of provider: acute and community trusts, GPs and social services; and between financial responsibilities and incentives: the health and local authority boundaries and individual and public responsibilities. There is a real absence of leadership in this key service area.

How change has been tackled

Given the extent of the challenge facing complex health service systems, a flexible, adaptive and dynamic approach to change is in fact required (Coote and Hunter, 1996). In the case of London, there is no doubt about the energy and ingenuity that have been invested in the change programme over the last five years by a variety of leaders.

Initially, a concerted package of 'top down' measures provided a lead. These included active political leadership from the Secretary of State; the six specialty reviews; ear-marked funding for transition, including price support to individual hospitals; more than £200 million of development funding for primary care; and special arrangements for negotiating change across local boundaries, such as the London Implementation Group and the London Initiative Zone.

At the same time, national policy introduced the 'internal market' into the NHS. This involved a number of complex and multi-faceted changes, including the introduction of the purchaser/provider split, the related reforms to community care and the merger of district health and family health service authorities to form the new health care commissioning authorities, as well as a dispersal of health commissioning power through GP fundholding. Put simply, the effect of these was to decentralise control while continuing to be strongly prescriptive from the centre on a whole range of issues of national concern. The series of national initiatives on mental health services discussed in Chapter 4 of this report is a good example of this phenomenon (Towell *et al.*, 1997).

Both sets of policies were taken forward by the many thousands of clinicians, managers and others working within and outside the NHS who have the capacity to shape particular initiatives locally. Case studies undertaken for the London Commission underline the extent to which development in London rests on the interaction of 'official' policy and its interpretation locally (Towell *et al.*, 1997).

This combination of official measures and the undoubted drive of many London leaders held out the promise of considerable progress, especially given the sustained political backing from within the Government. However, the evidence available to the London Commission suggests that the mixture of centralisation and decentralisation, control and autonomy within the health service system related poorly to the transformation in health services delivery that is in fact required. Insofar as the special policies and implementation arrangements for London have been helpful, most lost impetus early on. At the same time, the introduction of the internal market has hampered concerted city-wide action on a number of strategic issues and introduced perverse incentives for individual providers. Purchasers, who were new to their roles during this period, have been unable to counter these effectively. Their power is diluted by the complexity of London's health system and the strength of individual providers, and their needs assessment and service design capacities remain poorly developed (Millar, 1997a).

In terms of resources, it was undoubtedly a strength that special funding was available to meet bridging costs in the acute sector and promote development and innovation in primary and community services. However, primary care investment took place at such a pace that it was doubtful that local organisations were sufficiently prepared to ensure that it was well spent. At the same time, some of the large-scale changes to acute services, education and training are indefinitely delayed by difficulties with the PFI.

Overall, the fragmentation and competition characteristic of the internal market have added to the difficulty of delivering a change programme that requires sustained, integrated contributions from a number of service elements, professional bodies and institutions over a protracted period. It is clear that the development of local change agendas which harness commitment, energy and creativity around a coherent local approach has yet to be achieved in many parts of the capital (Towell *et al.*, 1997).

Finally, the continual churning of NHS structures and the rapid turnover of key managers have sapped the capacity and continuity necessary to build confidence in long-term service developments. The events of the last five years have highlighted the unintended effects and turbulence that structural changes bring in their wake. This has hampered the development of improved services for Londoners.

New approaches to health services development

All this implies that key actors and organisations will need to work in markedly different ways if further development in London's health services is to be achieved which reflects both government priorities and the need for appropriate local diversity. This requires shared understanding about the different types of changes that are needed across the capital and new ways of bringing them about. It also requires more effective collaboration locally to achieve significant changes in the pattern and nature of services and investment in developing and sustaining local leaders capable of seeing changes through. There needs to be much greater attention to involving the full range of relevant stakeholders, including clinicians and members of the public. These new ways of working will require a recasting of central/local relationships to provide the conditions for success.

The London Commission's work on the health system of London has underlined the complexity and uncertainty involved in shaping health service systems for the next century. With this come new requirements to collaborate across institutional boundaries and professional disciplines, to involve service users, local communities and clinicians and to apply evidence about effective practice and learning from evaluation. Given the extent of the uncertainties involved, service strategies and change programmes will need to adapt to new evidence and influences as they emerge (Harrison, 1997).

Three broad categories of change will be required if the capital's health services are to be successfully modernised for the next century. These are:

- **Large-scale changes to acute service configurations**

  Examples of this type of change include the creation of properly integrated specialty 'networks' across primary, secondary and tertiary care, as discussed in the Calman-Hine report on cancer care (Department of Health, 1995); the rationalisation of tertiary services and other acute services across a number of hospitals; and medical school mergers.

- **Changes designed to create new patterns of primary or community-based forms of care**

  Examples of this type of change include the next phase of strengthening primary care across whole districts, 'growing' new forms of primary care organisations capable of contributing to well-integrated programmes of care for individuals.

- **Local service developments**

  Examples of this type of change include the introduction of localised hospital-at-home schemes; some forms of urgent treatment in community settings; intermediate care and rehabilitation in local community hospitals and nursing homes; and the development of 24-hour mental health emergency assessment and home care services.

These different types of change need to be conceived of and achieved in quite different ways. The first two must take account of central priorities and constraints as well as what is feasible at local level. While major changes to the acute sector – for example, hospital mergers – are often very visible politically, changes to primary and community services are less constrained by political sensitivities at national level (Towell et al., 1997). Table 6.1 sets out the characteristics of these different types of change.

Table 6.1   Different types of service change

Type of change	Typical characteristics
Type 1 Relatively large-scale change intended to reshape the existing configuration of acute services (e.g. acute hospital mergers/restructuring)	• Large-scale usually involving multiple authorities and/or institutions • Long timescale; rarely less than three years, often more than five • High political visibility; involvement of national politicians/senior bureaucrats • Involves net withdrawal of resources for investment in other services • Local autonomy very constrained; local-centre tensions need to be managed • Public involvement/opinion largely a constraint
Type 2 Relatively large-scale change intended to create new patterns – or enhance existing patterns – of primary and community-based forms of care (e.g. the introduction of a network of primary care walk-in services linked to polyclinic facilities)	• Large-scale often involving multiple authorities and/or institutions • Relatively long timescale; rarely less than three years • Occasionally politically sensitive; relatively low visibility • Usually involves net investment of new resources as well as reuse of existing resources • More local autonomy but constrained by need to co-ordinate multiple authorities • Relatively high public/client involvement
Type 3 Relatively small-scale, very local service developments (e.g. the introduction of local 'hospital-at-home' services).	• Small-scale often linked to single authority and/or one or two institutions • Relatively short timescale; 6-24 months, although more time may be needed to achieve 'critical mass' • Usually not politically sensitive • Usually involves investment of new resources as well as reuse of existing resources • Relatively high degree of local autonomy • Relatively large scope for public involvement

Source: Towell *et al.* (1997)

A second important distinction in thinking about service change in London is between changes that are essentially about maintaining or improving existing service delivery – for example, reducing waiting times; providing 24-hour consultant cover in accident and emergency departments – and those that are essentially concerned with transforming or reinventing service delivery (see

Table 6.2 System improvement and transformational change

Type of change	System improvement	Transformational change
Type 1	Reducing outpatient waiting times across a whole sector of London	Rationalising tertiary and specialist services across a number of hospitals and using the resources saved to provide walk-in accident services
Type 2	Improving GP facilities and in so doing increasing the proportion of GPs working in group practices	Introducing a network of GP and nurse practitioner-led 24-hour walk-in clinics
Type 3	Increasing the utilisation of acute beds and theatres in the local DGH by reducing length of stay in a number of specialties	Closing a number of wards in the local DGH and reopening them as 'homeward-bound' facilities staffed by nurse practitioners in community settings

Source: Towell *et al.* (1997)

Table 6.2). Change of this second type includes the redevelopment of community hospitals to act as new intermediate-level facilities for the management of some types of urgent treatment; the introduction of a network of clinics providing walk-in primary care and direct access to diagnostic services and the creation of alternative forms of mental health crisis care for people from minority ethnic communities and for women.

This analysis highlights the fact that successful service development does not depend on conforming to a set formula or sequence of actions but is much more about understanding the context for change and of adopting different approaches in different circumstances. The case studies in change undertaken for the London Commission suggest that much is well understood and practised when the focus is system improvement (Towell *et al.*, 1997). The greater challenges lie in meeting the important but different requirements of politically sensitive large-scale change to acute services and the wide variety of service 'transformations' required to reshape health care in the capital to meet the diverse needs of Londoners.

Fostering transformational change in health services

Table 6.2 highlights the distinction between service changes that are designed to improve the performance of an existing organisation or system – for example, by reducing waiting times for outpatient appointments – and changes that transform the way the system performs, such as the introduction of 'walk-in' services that do away with waiting times. The factors which determine success in achieving these two types of change are often very different.

Experience suggests that there are special challenges to achieving system-wide changes that are different in degree and kind from those required to improve existing systems. Change at this level can involve developments such as:

- alliances and collaboration between individuals and agencies that have little to do with each other and therefore almost certainly have much to learn from each other – an example here might be closer links between NHS commissioners and those responsible for community regeneration schemes and local 'Agenda 21' initiatives;
- the building of 'cultural competence' and confidence among groups within the population who normally may not engage productively with the system but who may also have new, unfamiliar and useful perspectives to contribute;
- greater emphasis on learning from unfamiliar as well as familiar sources, on making new linkages across institutional and other boundaries and on sharing learning; and – critically –
- creating alliances of health authorities, trusts, primary care providers and others to collaborate on local service development issues at different levels.

Work of this kind is already taking place in parts of the capital, although it frequently lacks co-ordination, explicit policy frameworks and formal recognition. Particularly notable are moves by some health authorities, trusts and primary care organisations to establish collaborative groupings which might be termed 'local health economies', to provide a context for major changes in service provision across large population groups.

Alliances of this kind need to be fostered. Critically, they need to build the capacity to work collaboratively across existing institutional, professional and agency boundaries to create systems of inter-related services and to promote service co-ordination around individual users. These new ways of working locally require much more attention to involving relevant stakeholders – notably, clinicians and service users – in shaping and delivering change. They also require significant investment in developing and sustaining locally effective leadership capable of clearly articulating the need for change, challenging old assumptions and building commitment to new forms of practice (Towell *et al.*, 1997).

Recasting central/local relationships

Across the capital, acute services reconfiguration is a necessary first step to unlocking the existing pattern of service delivery and releasing resources for investment in other types of care. However, the experience of the last five years suggests that when the fragmentation and institutional focus characteristic of the internal market are mixed with attempts to impose 'top-down' plans agreed centrally, the processes involved become Byzantine and subject to frequent changes of tack. The resulting confusion means that they often fail to carry key stakeholders – notably, local people and NHS staff.

Central agencies classically relate to local organisations – in the NHS case, trusts or health authorities – through market mechanisms, as in the private sector, or through the 'top-down' planning characteristic of the public sector. These rest on hierarchical 'command-and-control' structures. The NHS 'internal market' displays an uneasy mixture of both types of central control.

The case material makes clear that every instance of major change (or lack of it) arises from a unique constellation of forces, constraints and events. There is nevertheless a broad pattern which underlies most politically sensitive changes. This is described in Figure 6.1.

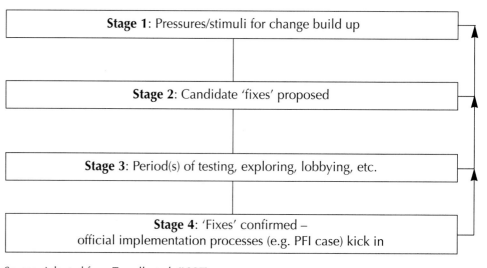

Source: Adapted from Towell et al. (1997)

Figure 6.1 Some generic stages in the process of realising major, politically significant change

Within the NHS, the scope for local autonomy is severely constrained by the need for central support to obtain capital and to make changes to the specialist medical workforce. This is particularly true for any major changes to the acute sector. In practice, the local role amounts to working with the centre to establish what is feasible and likely to be acceptable politically. Once this is reasonably clear, the official NHS machinery of business cases and human resources and estates planning can get underway to secure changes locally.

The history of change in London over the last five years suggests that this process is neither straightforward nor effective. The detailed case studies of change in London undertaken for the London Commission highlight the complexity of the extraneous factors, events and phenomena that influence how and whether change occurs. Because of this, the scope for detailed, externally imposed control is in practice very limited (Towell *et al.*, 1997).

In addition to this complexity, NHS central/local relationships display two further disadvantages. The first is that once a politically acceptable plan has been agreed, there is a tendency to adhere rigidly to it even when evidence emerges of serious defects. The second is that local consultation is reduced to a 'rubber-stamping' exercise to which local people and NHS staff cannot contribute effectively. This means that the collaboration and creativity required for successful implementation frequently fail to be generated locally.

Dysfunctional central/local relationships have hampered effective planning across London. They have posed a major obstacle to successful implementation of change locally. It is clear from this that they must be fundamentally recast.

This process needs to resolve the tension inherent between 'top-down' methods based on central control and 'bottom-up' approaches based on local initiative and energy by negotiating a middle way that combines the best features of both. The centre should be responsible for the broad context and direction-setting and for establishing a 'business style' based primarily on negotiation and mutual adjustment. Local agencies should take more responsibility for service design and development underpinned by the active participation of local people and NHS staff.

This requires:

- a central role for government in defining key parameters – notably, finance – and setting policy directions;
- enhanced efforts by government to ensure the consistency of strategic priorities, human resources and access to capital;

- government policy frameworks, incentive structures and monitoring arrangements which foster and reward effective joint action by local agencies, in particular between the NHS and local government;
- acceptance by government and local agencies that both will have requirements which – if not met – will stymie change. For government, these are likely to be around political requirements and standards such as equity. Locally they will centre on implementation problems such as transitional funding;
- new emphasis on – and investment in – health authorities' service design and development capacities;
- local efforts to establish partnerships between NHS purchasers, providers and other agencies, including local government, to pursue concerted action, including community regeneration and health services development in the interests of local populations;
- an emphasis throughout the system in promoting dialogue, building common values and encouraging greater transparency.

The essential approach is one of 'negotiation'. Central/local relationships of this type would contrast favourably with both the traditional 'command-and-control' structures of the NHS and its internal market variants (Towell *et al.*, 1997).

Conclusion

This chapter has addressed the 'how' of implementing change in London. It suggests that the political culture within which the NHS operates needs to be recast in two fundamental ways if the capital's health services are to be successfully modernised:

- central/local relationships for health services development need to move away from both 'market' mechanisms and traditional 'command-and-control' systems to ones based on negotiation within clear policy frameworks;

- health authorities, trusts and primary care organisations need to collaborate effectively with other interests to develop co-ordinated service systems designed to deliver well-integrated programmes of care calibrated to individual need. This might be done within 'local health economies' – that is, collaborative groupings involving the statutory authorities, clinicians, service users and other interested parties with a remit to develop integrated systems of care for large population groups across the capital.

CHAPTER 7

Recommendations

Imperatives for London

There are no 'quick fixes' or short cuts to improving health and health care in London. Instead, a new policy framework designed to support changes that benefit Londoners and engage their interest and enthusiasm is urgently required.

Delivering treatment, care and support correctly calibrated to individuals' needs is the nub of this. Integrating and ensuring continuity of care across the service system represents the fundamental challenge for the NHS and its local government partners at the turn of the century.

This must be done within individual neighbourhoods for the primary and community services which support people at home; at borough level to develop patterns of care and support for people with continuing disabilities and mental health needs; and across sectors of London to secure the reshaping of acute hospital provision and its relationship to primary and community care. Success depends on creating closer connections between the health service and local government, stronger links between clinicians practising in primary and in hospital settings, and increasing the influence of users and community groups in service design.

Addressing London's growing health inequalities and modernising health care delivery are pressing priorities. Five years into the London change programme, there is a serious log-jam. This report has demonstrated how capital shortages, the unmanageable complexities of current NHS planning arrangements and resistance to change have checked progress. Pressures from resource shortfalls and from changes to education, training and research are building up within the capital. These will force change in the medium and longer term. Action must be taken now to safeguard access to care for Londoners and the capital's position as a world centre for medical education and research.

A service development programme

The King's Fund London Commission has identified a programme of service development to transform health and health services across the capital.

- **The health of Londoners**

  For too long, debate on health in Britain has been dominated by discussion of the structures, organisation and financing of the National Health Service. The agenda for health services development within the NHS has been divorced from community development, urban regeneration and efforts from within local government and the private sector to create a sustainable London for the next century. Links must be forged to connect health care for individuals and communities with a strong public health strand within modern urban planning. London is the capital of the United Kindom and a world city. Health, health care and the development of London's health service infrastructure must play a part in the city's regeneration.

- **Primary care**

  A sustained development programme is needed if primary care in London is to play the central role in assessment, treatment and care co-ordination required by modern health systems. Recent changes in legislation have opened opportunities for developing primary care in entirely new ways. These require careful management by London's health commissioners if the capital is to equal the progress made in other parts of the country.

- **Rationalising London's hospital services**

  The piecemeal provision of medical and surgical specialties and emergency services across the capital needs to be replaced by networks which link primary, secondary and tertiary services within the different clinical specialties. London needs effective programmes of care, developed with and for individuals, and delivered with a new emphasis on continuity. London's university medical education and research centres must collaborate effectively with health authorities and trusts to ensure a sound basis for medical education and world class research.

- **Intermediate care**

  Rehabilitation, intensive home nursing, nursing homes and other 'intermediate care' services remain poorly developed in London. To ensure that Londoners retain local access to care, these services need to be planned across organisational, agency and political boundaries in collaboration with local government.

- **Mental health**

  Mental health urgently needs a sustained programme of service development. Special emphasis on aligning the contributions of health and social services; providing a full range of care, including rehabilitation, continuing, acute and crisis care; and meeting the needs of London's minority ethnic communities are all necessary. Meeting mental health needs in London's deprived communities will require increased resources as well as concerted collaboration between the NHS and local government.

- **Older people**

  The capital's health commissioners need to join with local government and with older Londoners themselves to plan more comprehensively for older citizens' well-being. This should concentrate on supporting older Londoners to remain fit, well and self-sustaining, and on securing continuity of care across the service system for older people who become ill or disabled. Appropriate care should be available according to clinical need, and age should not be a barrier to accessing it.

The King's Fund London Commission's recommendations centre on the policies required to support the development programme it has identified. These policies cover:

- **public health in London;**
- **a new strategic framework to support health services development in the capital;**
- **new mechanisms for allocating resources;**
- **human resources policies which are firmly linked to service development.**

These policies must be combined with the new style of collaborative central/local and inter-agency working outlined in Chapter 6. This means replacing the uneasy combination of 'command-and-control' and 'market-management' that has characterised relationships under the internal market with a new and transparent style of negotiation with central government. This must be firmly tied to effective local collaboration.

The Commission's recommendations concentrate on *functions* that need to be undertaken within London if positive change is to result. The Commission considers that, wherever possible, these should be undertaken by existing health service or local government structures. These should be resourced to carry them out effectively.

1. Public health policies for London

1.1 The Commission recommends that new public health responsibilities for the capital and specific functions for regulating health service provision be created within the Government Office for London. Once decisions on the future of London government and its relationship with central government and the London boroughs have been taken, public health responsibilities would be incorporated into the new structures agreed for the capital.

The intention is not to replace the role of London's health authorities but to augment them by giving new responsibilities for health to London government. This would amount to a 21st century reworking of the role of Medical Officer of Health, with responsibility for the whole of the capital. This new function within London government should cover both the interactions between environmental, transport, housing, employment and other policies that contribute to healthy living for Londoners and responsibilities for monitoring and assessing formal health services. This will involve:

1.2 Developing a public health strategy for Londoners, building on community development initiatives which link local government and local health services in community regeneration and renewal of the urban fabric. This strategy would need to address the capital's growing health inequalities as one of its major priorities, and should take account of interactions between health services and other factors impacting on health, such as transport, housing, employment, and environmental issues.

London's health authorities and boroughs should collaborate closely in the development of this city-wide programme, which should be firmly linked to existing work on urban renewal, 'Agenda 21' and other policies designed to create a sustainable city for the next century. One of its explicit aims should be to link spending on health care infrastructure with the regeneration of the capital. The NHS is scheduled to spend over £1.5 billion on capital projects within the city over the next five years. Steps should be taken to ensure that this investment is used strategically, to make a major contribution to the renewal of London's urban fabric.

1.3 Undertaking a major programme to facilitate public understanding and involvement in the modernisation of health care in the capital. This would build public understanding of and commitment to the changing shape of health care and the choices which need to be made within the NHS.

1.4 Providing a monitoring and information role for health and health care in London by working with health authorities and providers to improve the comparability, relevance and timeliness of data collection so as to allow useful comparisons to be made across the capital.

1.5 Independent assessment and regulation of health services in the capital, in a manner similar to the role that the Office for Standards in Education (Ofsted) performs within the education sector, with the aim of ensuring that changes to the system of health care delivery in the capital lead to improved health for Londoners.

2. A new strategic framework for health services development

The lack of strategic direction, appropriate rules and incentives within the London change programme has been a major problem in recent years. The Commission's recommendations concentrate on the need to establish initiatives and leadership – with specific powers – at appropriate levels within the system. This is not an argument for central planning; indeed, it recognises that London's diversity requires local solutions to service problems.

The geographical basis for service development will vary according to the task. Primary and intermediate care planning is probably best undertaken very locally, on a patch or locality basis; mental health and older people's services should be planned borough-wide to foster the closest possible connection between the NHS and local government. Acute specialty planning requires effective collaboration across and between the health authorities and trusts within the 'sectors' of London's five medical education and research centres.

In each case, planning should be understood as a participative and creative process of making progress within a broadly agreed strategic direction, rather than detailed prescription. Progress depends on clear frameworks for local service development from the NHS Executive and on greatly enhanced capacity within London's local health economies to collaborate on service development.

Policy framework

2.1. The Commission recommends that local progress is guided within clear development and investment frameworks established and monitored by the NHS Executive, which would also hold responsibility for negotiating local plans for the Commission's service development programme with London's health authorities. The establishment of such a framework depends critically on a move away from the 'command-and-control' and quasi-market methods characteristic of recent years. Instead, a new political culture based on negotiation and transparency needs to be established between central government and the groupings of interests the Commission has termed 'local health economies' (see Chapter 6). In turn, these local coalitions need to seek joint commitment to agendas for major change. Financial and other incentives must be reshaped to foster inter-agency collaboration. Local progress should be monitored by the NHS Executive using clear development objectives framed around the central requirement of improving the health of Londoners. Recommendations from the Commission's special studies on mental health and older people provide more detail on how this should be done (see Chapters 4 and 5 and the discussion below).

2.2. The Commission recommends that where local service strategies involve joint commissioning, health authorities and local government are jointly monitored on the progress they have achieved.

2.3. The Commission recommends a system of performance-related objectives for health service organisations and individual managers relating to a coherent London-wide change programme, with measurable goals which are consistent across the capital. Responsibility for monitoring the effectiveness of these would rest with the NHS Executive. The health of Londoners, rather than the survival or growth of particular organisations, must guide this.

Strengthening local commissioning

Progress depends on increasing the capacity of local health agencies to undertake commissioning in its true sense. This means reshaping patterns of health services provision and the processes of delivery to best meet individual and population needs. The diversity of health needs and the variety of current service configurations within different parts of the city mean that any attempt at a 'London-wide blueprint' for the Commission's service development programme would fail. Services must be planned to meet city-wide objectives, but particular approaches must be developed and implemented locally, with the full participation of Londoners and NHS staff.

2.4 The Commission recommends that health commissioning in London is strengthened by enhancing health authorities' needs assessment and service development and design capacities. Critically, health authorities must develop the ability to collaborate with key stakeholders to design and plan the delivery of integrated programmes of care around the needs of individuals and communities, and evaluate their effectiveness.

2.5 The Commission recommends that special development agencies be established to support primary care and mental health in the capital. These should centre on disseminating learning about effective development and pooling knowledge about problem-solving. A prime objective should be to foster the collaborative approach outlined in Chapter 6. Clinical and service user involvement will be essential. These development agencies could be sponsored by the NHS Executive; by London health authorities collectively or by consortia of health authorities in the different London sectors. They should have dedicated resources, ideally through a special allocation from central government, as well as clear terms of reference and objectives. These should encompass London-wide information and performance management frameworks for these key services. Progress on achieving objectives should be evaluated.

3. New mechanisms for allocating resources

Revenue

If health services are to remain comprehensive and free at the point of delivery, the Commission considers that the funding available to the NHS overall will need to grow at a rate which will match demographic changes, rising demand and technological advances within modern medicine.

Those responsible for commissioning health care for Londoners should have a *fair* level of resources in the context of a nationally equitable allocation. This should be determined on the basis of population needs and costs of provision. The current formula for allocating resources, which relates mainly to services provided under HCHS programmes, has been criticised on the grounds that insufficient weight is given to the needs of deprived inner-city populations. But to be effective, the whole health budget, including hospital, community and family health services must be distributed in a fair and consistent manner.

Although allocations from central government to local authorities are not generally earmarked for particular client groups, it is important that there is consistency behind health authority and local authority funding mechanisms. Separate budgetary systems create disincentives for collaboration and joint working. This applies to primary and secondary care within the health service, and it also operates between health and local authorities. A prime example is cost shunting between health and local authorities over the care of older people.

3.1 The Commission recommends a reassessment of the formula for the allocation of financial resources to health authorities aimed at combining the budgets for hospital and community health services (HCHS) with that for family health services (FHS). This would ensure a consistent approach to the allocation of resources, which is currently lacking. Such a reassessment would result in a greater allocation of resources to inner-city health authorities, including those in London. The current situation for FHS, based as it is on patterns of general practice provision, allocates fewer resources to the capital than a needs-based formula consistent with the national approach to HCHS allocations would require. The needs of present-day populations should determine resource levels.

3.2 The Commission recommends that national resource allocation formulae be adjusted to reflect the special intensity of mental health and other health needs in London and other inner cities.

3.3 The Commission recommends the establishment of a review of the relationship between funding streams for health care and social care with a view to their complete overhaul. This would allow the design of a better system of incentives for coherent working across provider boundaries. As part of this review, the Commission recommends that local authorities' standard spending assessment formulae be examined to assess whether they adequately reflect the needs of special client groups, especially older people. At the same time, the assumptions on which the transfer of funds from the Social Security budget to local authorities took place (Special Transitional Grant) should be re-examined and adjustments made where required. Special attention should be paid to obtaining consistency between local authority and health authority funding formulae.

3.4 The Commission recommends that health and local authorities be empowered to pool budgets to secure clearly defined service objectives and development programmes – for example, in implementing jointly agreed strategies and commissioning plans for mental health and older people.

Capital

The provision of capital for public sector health care is an issue of fundamental importance. The Private Finance Initiative (PFI) has failed to deliver any investment in London's hospitals and medical schools so far. Investment in London is complicated by the size and number of potential schemes and their interconnectedness. There is a need to examine the current PFI process so as to determine what the potential benefits are for London and to test if these might be delivered in a more cost-effective way.

The present scheme-by-scheme arrangements are inefficient in terms of the transactions costs involved. Further, pursuing a multiplicity of schemes across the capital undermines any attempt to secure a London-wide strategy and is very likely to build up affordability problems in the medium and longer term. The partnership between private finance and the public sector should develop in ways which ensure:

- value for money at each stage of the procurement process for NHS infrastructure, including facilities management services, if these are included;

- a strategic approach to investment in health services infrastructure recognising the need for prioritisation of schemes within the still constrained level of capital available to the NHS in London;
- a greater level of accountability to the public for capital schemes;
- the appropriate pooling of risk in the development of NHS infrastructure;
- sufficient flexibility to deal with the uncertainties of future demand for health care services.

3.5 The Commission recommends that an independent agency be created with public service objectives to develop an investment programme for NHS infrastructure in London within the strategic framework determined by the NHS Executive. This new agency would work in partnership with private sector lenders to create a city-wide strategic plan and investment programme. This would substantially reduce transactions costs and spread the risks across a wider number of schemes, giving lenders more security and reducing costs to the public sector. Pooling of this sort would give the NHS greater overall flexibility, and build in incentives to keep individual schemes modest. The agency would own the buildings and lease them to the NHS in London.

The Commission sees no reason in principle why this form of capital acquisition should not be considered 'off the public balance sheet', and thus not constitute a part of the Public Sector Borrowing Requirement. The new agency might also seek funding from the public, by issuing 'London Health Bonds' with an appropriate rate of return. If these could be associated with particular schemes, this could be seen as a way of encouraging communities to invest in local health services.

Medical education and research

There must be common assumptions and logic underlying the ways in which medical education, research and services develop. Progress in education, training and research must complement service developments rather than diverge from or determine them.

3.6 The Commission recommends that public sector capital funds be made available to ensure the development of sites for the four merged medical education and research centres in London, and that these be progressed as quickly as is feasible. These mergers of institutions are essential to London's ability to maintain international excellence in medical education and research into the next century. It would be a serious mistake to permit the current commitment to wane because of a failure to provide capital investment.

3.7 The Commission recommends that London's research and education centres collaborate actively with health authorities to design the networks of organisations and clinicians required to deliver integrated programmes of care to Londoners. These programmes must go beyond the boundaries of individual institutions and include a strong element of workforce planning.

4. Human resources policies

This report has highlighted the way that rising public expectations, quality considerations and technological changes are forcing change to health services delivery. The recent changes to postgraduate medical education will also exert a powerful influence on patterns of health service staffing, and these have yet to be thought through. Chronic shortages of staff, recruitment problems and poor morale suggest that education, workforce planning, training and support structures are insufficiently equipped to cope with the pressure and pace of change.

4.1 The Commission recommends the establishment of a London-wide review to examine the impact of the 'Calman' changes to medical training on medical and nursing skill-mix, role demarcation and staffing arrangements within and between trusts, to report on good practice and desirable ways forward across the capital within 12 months. This initiative should be sponsored by the NHS Executive.

4.2 The Commission recommends the development of more flexible and, where appropriate, joint training arrangements to facilitate more effective use of skills, improved understanding, co-ordination and teamworking between health and social care staff from different professional backgrounds. This is particularly important for members of community teams. Service users and their families need to be actively involved in training and development programmes.

Within each of the Commission's six service development programmes, London trusts should collaborate with their social services counterparts on the introduction of new job descriptions for posts which combine various aspects of health service and/or social care practitioner. These should recognise the need to redefine the nature of service provision around the needs of service users and to foster greatly improved integration and continuity of care. This particularly applies to people with continuing disabilities, who find dealing with a multiplicity of professionals dysfunctional.

Recommendations on mental health and older people

The Commission has paid particular attention to mental health and older people in London, and conducted special studies on them. There are a number of recommendations relating to these areas. Although these are recorded in Chapters 4 and 5, they are summarised in Box 7.1.

The approach within these two service areas is consistent with the overall recommendations of the Commission. Both special studies stress the need to develop inclusive strategies for vulnerable groups that emphasise health promotion and links between health services development and city-wide community development and regeneration strategies. The negotiation of collaborative local plans between health and local authorities and other members of the local health economy is central to sound service development. New approaches to human resources questions and effective care and treatment strategies are also highlighted. So is a requirement to develop more holistic care-planning approaches in which the importance of continuity of care for individuals is recognised.

Conclusion

Repeated attempts to reform London's health services and medical education have been made throughout this century. As it ends, supporting Londoners' health and modernising health services in the capital remain formidable challenges. To meet them, the King's Fund London Commission has formulated a series of recommendations for policies to support a major service development programme.

The Commission considers that this programme offers the best chance of making necessary changes to improve the health and health services available to Londoners. To be effective, it must go together with a fundamental recasting of the political culture within which the NHS operates. Major changes to public health, resource allocation and human resources policies are critical, as well as a new strategic framework for health services development.

The King's Fund London Commission has worked constructively with a range of stakeholders across the city in developing its report and recommendations. In the same collaborative spirit, the Commission presents its recommendations to the Government, to the Executive of the National Health Service, and to everyone working within and outside health services and local government in London with an interest in health, as well as to Londoners themselves.

> ## BOX 7.1: RECOMMENDATIONS ON MENTAL HEALTH AND OLDER PEOPLE IN LONDON
>
> ### Mental health
>
> *Public health approaches to London's mental health*
> - Mental health services development should be reframed within a wider, more inclusive approach to mental health within national and city-wide policies. This should include action to promote mental health and reduce the social and environmental stresses that contribute to mental illness.
>
> - Within London, community and borough development and regeneration programmes need consciously to include measures to support the mental health of Londoners.
>
> *Local mental health plans*
> - Development of joint commissioning approaches between health and local authority social services and housing departments is an urgent priority in London. This should be facilitated by moves by central government to encourage the pooling of NHS and local authority allocations for local mental health services, and the development of appropriate accountability mechanisms.
>
> - Health authorities and local government should be required to produce costed and timetabled local mental health plans jointly. Local service developments should be identified collaboratively between health and local authorities and local providers, with full user and community involvement, to include the voluntary and private sectors.
>
> - Plans should be based around the functions that services deliver for the people they serve, rather than on service 'models'.
>
> - Health and local authorities' progress in achieving the goals identified in local plans should be jointly monitored by the NHS Executive and the Social Services Inspectorate.
>
> - NHS trusts should be encouraged to provide 'social' care, to be funded from local authority allocations, in order to encourage more coherent service provision.
>
> - Practical care planning processes should be devised with the explicit purpose of connecting the planning of health and social care for individuals with the realities of the whole of their lives, to include housing and employment.
>
> - Major improvements in current information and monitoring systems are required. These should be better standardised across providers to ensure that meaningful comparisons can be made between them and across authorities and statutory and voluntary sector providers.
>
> *Resource allocation*
> - Allocation formulae should over time be adjusted to ensure equity based on socio-demographic and epidemiological factors. The special intensity of mental health needs in the inner city should be recognised.
>
> *cont.*

Human resources
- Exploration, review and debate of professional roles and accountabilities within community mental health services should take place, preferably at the instigation of the professions themselves, but with full participation of service users and other stakeholder groups.

- Urgent work needs to be undertaken on ways of attracting and retaining mental health professionals to work in London. This should include an appreciation of appropriate ways of supporting staff in their work in the inner-city.

- Concerted attempts to improve the cultural competence of mental health services across London are required. These should include appropriate training and recruitment strategies.

New knowledge
- Evaluation of the effectiveness of intensive 24-hour community services to prevent admission or reduce the length of stay within psychiatric inpatient provision should be commissioned.

- Research of effective helping strategies and treatments for people from minority ethnic communities should be commissioned, in partnership with representatives from those communities.

Older people

Public health policies for older people in London
- The health and social care of older people should be reframed within a wider, more inclusive approach to the well-being of older people within national and city-wide policies. This will require greatly improved policy co-ordination for social security and environmental policies as well as health and social care.

- Within London, community and borough development and regeneration programmes need consciously to include measures to support the well-being of older Londoners. If this approach is to be successful, it must encompass the full range of community interests and resources, including community safety.

Local plans for older people's services
- Development of joint commissioning approaches between health and local authority, social services and housing departments is an urgent priority in London. This needs to be facilitated through moves by central government to encourage the pooling of NHS and local authority expenditures on local services, and the development of appropriate accountability mechanisms.

- Health and local government should be required to produce costed and timetabled local plans for the development of older people's services. These should cover community development and other initiatives designed to promote the well-being of older people.

cont.

- These plans should be based around the functions and outcomes that services deliver for older people, rather than on service 'models'. They should include appropriately phased investments in new or additional service elements, which should be firmly linked to financial and business plans. Standards for access to treatment should be set within the plans, and closely monitored.

- Major improvements in current information and monitoring systems are required to permit care to be better integrated around the needs of individual older people.

- Information should be better standardised across providers to ensure that meaningful comparisons can be made between them.

- As investments are made and services developed, there should be a conscious effort to assess their impact on the system as a whole. Audit, evaluation, computer modelling techniques and simulations may prove helpful here, along with the development of integrated care pathways designed around users' needs and experiences.

Resource allocation
- Allocation formulae should be adjusted over time to ensure equity based on socio-demographic and epidemiological factors. It may well be, for example, that formulae should become more sensitive to the proportions of the very old within the population and of older people living alone.

Human resources
- Education, training and recruitment policies designed to encourage culturally competent services for older people should be put in place.

APPENDICES

Membership of the King's Fund London Commission

Lord Hussey (Chairman)

Pearl Brown

Brendan Devlin

Baroness Eccles of Moulton

Professor Sir David Goldberg

Professor Richard Himsworth

Baroness Jay *(resigned May 1997 on her appointment to Government)*

Professor Eve Johnstone

Robert Maxwell

Professor John Pattison

Peter Westland

Seán Boyle (Research Manager)

Virginia Beardshaw (Secretary)

Terms of reference

The following were established as terms of reference for the King's Fund London Commission in September 1995:

1. The Commission's objective is to suggest a comprehensive pattern of health services that will serve London well in the 21st century, and to make proposals on how to move towards that pattern.

2. The Commission's main focus will be on service requirements, based on the health needs of Londoners. It will also take account of future undergraduate and postgraduate education and research.

3. The aim will be for a pattern of health services of high quality, capable of continuing adjustment. It will also focus on strengthening London's role as an international centre of medical excellence.

4. In carrying out its task, the Commission will review:

   - Its own report, *London Health Care 2010*, published in June 1992
   - The Tomlinson Report published in October 1992
   - The Government's response to Tomlinson entitled *Making London Better*
   - Other key policy documents
   - The London scene as it presents now
   - The situation in other cities, in the UK and elsewhere

5. It will also consider what has happened in London since its first report, the capacity of the NHS to handle these changes, and where they seem likely to lead. The Commission will thus be concerned with the management of change as well as with a desired pattern of services.

6. The Commission will obtain research reports on which to base its conclusions and will make these public as its work proceeds. The Commission hopes that it will conclude its work and issue its final report within about 18 months from the present date.

The work of the King's Fund London Commission

The work of the King's Fund London Commission rests on a comprehensive programme of analysis of health and social services in London. Research reports on five major themes were produced and published for the Commission. A number of background papers were commissioned for these major research reports. All of these are listed below.

The five research reports are:

London's Mental Health, Sonia Johnson, Graham Thornicroft, Rosalind Ramsay, Liz Brooks (Institute of Psychiatry), Paul Lelliot (Royal College of Psychiatrists), Edward Peck, Helen Smith (Centre for Mental Health Services Development), Daniel Chisolm (Institute of Psychiatry), Bernard Audini (Royal College of Psychiatrists), Martin Knapp and David Goldberg (Institute of Psychiatry) (eds).

The London Health Care System, Anthony Harrison (King's Fund).

The Health and Care of Older People in London, Tony Warnes (School of Health and Related Research, University of Sheffield).

London Health Care: Rethinking Development, David Towell, Gordon Best and Steve Pashley (King's Fund).

The Health Economy of London, Seán Boyle and Richard Hamblin (King's Fund).

Mental health

Huw Richards, King's Fund, co-ordinated the work on mental health and chaired the Mental Health Support Group.

Members of the Mental Health Support Group:

Dr Bernard Audini	(Royal College of Psychiatrists)
Seán Boyle	(King's Fund)
Daniel Chisholm	(Institute of Psychiatry)
Sue Gallagher	(Merton, Sutton and Wandsworth Health Authority)
Professor Sir David Goldberg	**(London Commission)**
Dr Sonia Johnson	(Institute of Psychiatry)
Professor Martin Knapp	(Institute of Psychiatry)
Dr Paul Lelliott	(Royal College of Psychiatrists)
Edward Peck	(Centre for Mental Health Services Development)
Dr Rosalind Ramsay	(Institute of Psychiatry)
Huw Richards (Chair)	**(King's Fund)**
Helen Smith	(Centre for Mental Health Services Development)
Professor Graham Thornicroft	(Institute of Psychiatry)
Professor Peter Tyrer	(St Mary's Hospital Medical School)
Charles Waddicor	(London Borough of Sutton)
Peter Westland	**(London Commission)**

Research papers:

Londoners' mental health needs: the sociodemographic context. Sonia Johnson, Rosalind Ramsay and Graham Thornicroft (Institute of Psychiatry)

London in the context of mental health policy. Paul Lelliot, Bernard Audini (Royal College of Psychiatrists), Sonia Johnson (Institute of Psychiatry) and Hilary Guite (King's College Hospital School of Medicine and Dentistry)

Mental health services for older people in London. Michael Philpot (Maudsley Hospital) and Sube Banerjee (Institute of Psychiatry)

Child and adolescent services in London. Veira Bailey (Hounslow and Spelthorne Community and Mental Health Services NHS Trust)

Substance misuse services in London. Michael Farrell, Jane Marshall (Maudsley Hospital) and John Strang (Institute of Psychiatry)

Consultation-liaison psychiatry services in London. Tom Sensky (Charing Cross and Westminster Medical School), Amanda Ramirez (United Medical and Dental Schools), Simon Wessely (King's College Hospital School of Medicine and Dentistry) and Peter White (The Medical Colleges of St Bartholomew's and Royal London Hospital)

Services in London for HIV/AIDS-related mental health needs. Jose Catalan (Charing Cross and Westminster Medical School)

Services for mentally disordered offenders. Hilary Guite (King's College Hospital School of Medicine and Dentistry) and Vida Field (Lambeth, Southwark and Lewisham Health Authority)

The homeless in London. Dinesh Bhugra (Institute of Psychiatry)

Mental health services in primary care in London. Shaun Kerwick (United Medical and Dental Schools). André Tylee and David Goldberg (Institute of Psychiatry)

London's ethnic minorities and the provision of mental health services. Kamaldeep Bhui (Institute of Psychiatry)

Mental health services in London: evidence from research and routine data. Sonia Johnson (Institute of Psychiatry) and Paul Lelliott (Royal College of Psychiatrists)

Levels of in-patient and residential provision throughout London. Rosalind Ramsay, Graham Thornicroft, Sonia Johnson, Liz Brooks and Gyles Glover (Institute of Psychiatry)

The structure and functioning of London's mental health services. Sonia Johnson, Liz Brooks, Rosalind Ramsay and Graham Thornicroft (Institute of Psychiatry)

A functional approach to assessing services: the DISC framework. Helen Smith and Edward Peck (Centre for Mental Health Services Development)

London in close-up: the spectrum of care in three London catchment areas. Thomas Becker, Sarah Bixby, Sonia Johnson, Rosalind Ramsay and Graham Thornicroft (Institute of Psychiatry)

Mental health services in London: costs. Daniel Chisolm, Ana Lowin and Martin Knapp (Institute of Psychiatry)

The obstacles to and the opportunities for the development of mental health services in London: the perceptions of managers. Edward Peck, Helen Smith, Ingrid Barker and Gregor Henderson (Centre for Mental Health Services Development)

Health care systems

Anthony Harrison, King's Fund, co-ordinated the work on health care systems and chaired the Health Care Systems Support Group.

Members of the Health Care Systems Support Group:

Seán Boyle	(King's Fund)
Brendan Devlin	**(London Commission)**
George Gibson	(Merton, Sutton and Wandsworth Health Authority)
Peter Gluckman	(Lambeth, Southwark and Lewisham Health Authority)

Nilesh Goswami	(MHA)
Christine Farrell	(King's Fund)
Anthony Harrison (Chair)	**(King's Fund)**
Professor Richard Himsworth	**(London Commission)**
John James	(King's College Hospital)
Jacqueline Mallender	(MHA)
Val Martin	(Lewisham Hospital)
Professor John Pattison	**(London Commission)**
Diane Plamping	(King's Fund)

Research papers:

A Survey of Needs Assessment Activities in London Health Authorities. Naomi Fulop (Policy Studies Institute) and Martin Hensher (London Health Economics Consortium)

A Survey of Acute Hospital Configuration in London. Jacqueline Mallender and Nilesh Goswami (MHA)

Primary Care in London. Virginia Morley (Independent Healthcare Consultant), Peter Holland and Rebecca Scott (Lambeth, Southwark and Lewisham Health Authority)

Intermediate Care: A conceptual framework and review of the literature. Andrea Steiner (University of Southampton)

A Capital Conundrum: The effect of the Private Finance Initiative on strategic change in London's health care. Richard Meara (Meara Management Consultancy)

Accident and Emergency Care at the Primary-Secondary Interface. Emilie Roberts and Nicholas Mays (King's Fund).

Hubs, spokes and policy cycles: An analysis of the policy implications for the NHS of changes to medical staffing. Chris Ham, Judith Smith and John Temple (Health Services Management Centre, University of Birmingham)

Older people

Richard Poxton, King's Fund, co-ordinated the work on older people and chaired the Older People Support Group.

Members of the Older People Support Group:

Virginia Beardshaw	**(Secretary, London Commission)**
Seán Boyle	(King's Fund)
Pearl Brown	**(London Commission)**
Linda Challis	(Oxford Brookes University)
Gillian Dalley	(Centre for Policy on Ageing)
Shah Ebrahim	(Royal Free Hospital School of Medicine)
Professor Richard Himsworth	**(London Commission)**
John Hollis	(London Research Centre)
Paula Jones	(Age Concern London)

Doreen Kenny	(London Research Centre)
Jackie Morris	(Royal Free Hospital and School of Medicine)
Denise Platt	(Association of Metropolitan Authorities)
Richard Poxton (Chair)	**(King's Fund)**
Richard Stanton	(Association of London Government)
Tony Warnes	(University of Sheffield)

Research papers:

Health and Social Care Provision for London's black and minority ethnic older population. Tahera Aanchawan (King's Fund) and Saber Khan (University of Westminster)
Towards an analysis of the health and social care needs of older Londoners. Linda Challis and Joanne Pearson (Oxford Brookes University)
Health status and health care utilisation amongst elderly persons in Britain. Maria Evandrou (King's Fund)
The demography of older people in London. John Hollis (London Research Centre)
A review of services for older people in London. Kenneth Howse and Gillian Dalley (Centre for Policy on Ageing)
Estimating Levels of Need among Older People in London. Doreen Kenny (London Research Centre)
Trends in Social Services Activity, Staffing and Expenditure in relation to Older People in London. Doreen Kenny (London Research Centre)
Users' Views of Local Health Services for Older People in London. Kate Mortimer (Centre for Policy on Ageing)
Summary of commissioned thematic papers. Richard Poxton (King's Fund)
Local Authority Financial Resources. Richard Stanton and Mark Brangwyn (Association of London Government)
Irish Older People in London. Mary Tilki (Federation of Irish Societies and Middlesex University)

Minority ethnic communities

Tahera Aanchawan, King's Fund, co-ordinated the Support Group on Minority Ethnic Communities

Tahara Aanchawan	(King's Fund)
Seán Boyle	(King's Fund)
Yvonne Christie	(Independent Consultant)
Naaz Coker	(King's Fund)
Zaide Crowe Kente	(London Voluntary Sector Resource Centre)
John James	(King's College Hospital)
Parimala Moodley	(Pathfinder NHS Trust)
Shushila Patel	(NHS Executive)
Mike Silvera	(London Health and Race Purchasers Forum)
Lydia Yee	(Independent Consultant)

Rethinking development

David Towell, King's Fund, co-ordinated the work on rethinking development and chaired the Rethinking Development Support Group.

Members of the Rethinking Development Support Group:

Virginia Beardshaw	**(Secretary, London Commission)**
Gordon Best	(King's Fund)
Seán Boyle	(King's Fund)
Pearl Brown	**(London Commission)**
Baroness Eccles	**(London Commission)**
Robert Maxwell	**(London Commission)**
Steve Pashley	(King's Fund)
David Towell (Chair)	**(King's Fund)**

Baroness Jay provided valuable advice to Seán Boyle and Richard Hamblin in their efforts to produce *The Health Economy of London*. Finally, the research effort of the Commission was guided by a Research Advisory Group chaired by Professor Brian Jarman. The members of this group were:

Virginia Beardshaw	**(Secretary, London Commission)**
Seán Boyle	(King's Fund)
Angela Coulter	(King's Fund)
Professor Brian Jarman (Chair)	**(St Mary's Medical School)**
Linda Jarrett	(King's Fund)
Ken Judge	(King's Fund)
Robert Maxwell	**(London Commission)**
Nicholas Mays	(King's Fund)
David Towell	(King's Fund)
Ian Wylie	(King's Fund)

Geographical sectors of London

In this report parts of London are referred to in two ways: first, according to district health authorities within a particular geographic sector. These are defined as north west, north central, east, south east and south, and correspond approximately to the spheres of influence of the five groupings of medical schools in London, extended to the borders of the capital.

The second is a grouping by type of socio-economic area, based on a statistical classification of district health authorities which clusters them according to their similarity on a number of socio-economic and demographic characteristics derived from the 1991 Census. This classification allows comparison with corresponding groupings in the rest of England. Three types of group are defined: inner-deprived, mixed-status and high-status. Lists of London district health authorities classified by sector and by socio-economic type are provided below. For a more detailed description including the rest of England, see *The Health Economy of London* (Boyle and Hamblin, 1997).

Geographic Sectors

North West
Kensington, Chelsea and Westminster
Ealing, Hammersmith and Hounslow
Brent and Harrow
Hillingdon

North Central
Camden and Islington
Enfield and Haringey
Barnet

Socio-economic Areas

Inner-deprived
Kensington, Chelsea and Westminster
Camden and Islington
East London and the City
Lambeth, Southwark and Lewisham

Mixed-status
Ealing, Hammersmith and Hounslow
Brent and Harrow
Enfield and Haringey
Redbridge and Waltham Forest
Merton, Sutton and Wandsworth

East
East London and the City
Redbridge and Waltham Forest
Barking and Havering

South East
Lambeth, Southwark and Lewisham
Bexley and Greenwich
Bromley

South
Merton, Sutton and Wandsworth
Kingston and Richmond
Croydon

High-status
Hillingdon
Barnet
Barking and Havering
Bexley and Greenwich
Bromley
Kingston and Richmond
Croydon

Specialty reviews

Cardiac Services Review

The specialty review chaired by Professor Geoffrey Smith advocated a reduction in the number of cardiac centres from 14 to nine, arguing that not one centre in London met all the criteria for model cardiac centres and many fell a long way short. There was therefore a 'clear case for rationalisation to create fewer, larger and stronger centres'.

Specific recommendations

North-west

- Expand adult services at the Royal Brompton Hospital, including transfer of services from Hammersmith Hospital with the Hammersmith Hospital site closed, on the understanding that the Royal Brompton Hospital becomes an integral part of a management of the Chelsea and Westminster Hospital
- Transfer services from Harefield Hospital to a new centre at Northwick Park Hospital with Harefield Hospital closing
- St Mary's Hospital to stay open until the capacity of Royal Brompton Hospital and Northwick Park Hospital sites to cope with demand proven
- Paediatric cardiac services to be transferred to Great Ormond Street Hospital and Guy's and St Thomas's Hospital Trust

North-central

- Expand services at Middlesex Hospital, if not feasible because of space, then evaluate options
- Expand paediatric cardiac services at Great Ormond Street Hospital

---

NOTE: In this appendix the following codes have been adopted to identify the current position:

- where the position in a sector is still uncertain, the text is underlined;
- where a plan has been agreed but is not yet implemented the text is unembellished;
- where a plan is subject to PFI this is shown in bold;
- where a plan has been agreed and implemented the text is italicised.

East

- Expand service at Royal London Hospital and the London Chest Hospital
- Close service at St Bartholomew's Hospital
- Evaluate possibility of new service in Essex

South-east

- Rationalise Guy's and St Thomas's Hospital Trust to one site and expand, recommendation being Guy's Hospital
- Close service at the Brook Hospital
- Expand services at King's College Hospital
- Consider a new centre in Brighton

South

- Retain and expand service at St George's Hospital

Current position

North-west

Still uncertain, discussions between trusts involved and Imperial College of Medicine still ongoing. Royal Brompton Hospital remains a separate trust. Unlikely that Northwick Park Hospital will be venue of specialist clinical and research services currently taking place at Harefield Hospital.

North-central

Business case for redevelopment of University College Hospitals London Trust includes intention to develop cardiac service in line with cardiac review. **Redeveloped University College Hospitals London Trust planned for 2001, subject to PFI.**

East

St Bartholomew's Hospital and London Chest Hospital remain sites until the completion of the Whitechapel redevelopment in 2002, subject to PFI.

South-east

Inpatient services to be centralised at St Thomas's Hospital with 80 per cent of Brook Hospital workload being transferred to here (remainder to King's Hospital). Service remains split while St Thomas's Hospital is refurbished.

South

New unit at St George's Hospital due for completion by November 2000.

Cancer Services Review

The review of cancer services chaired by Dr Christopher Paine advocated that the number of specialist centres should be reduced from 14 to eight. These should be better staffed and equipped.

Specific recommendations

North-west

- Maintain services at both Charing Cross Hospital and Hammersmith
- Charing Cross Hospital to be the main unit for the sector, linked to Hammersmith Hospital, serving in total 1.75 million people
- The Royal Marsden Hospital, Fulham Road to be transferred to the Royal Marsden Hospital, Sutton
- St George's Hospital and the Royal Marsden Hospital to merge
- Mount Vernon Hospital to be retained

North-central

- Enlarge service at University College Hospital/Middlesex Hospital
- Transfer services from the Royal Free Hospital
- Expand service at the North Middlesex Hospital

East

- Combine the Royal London Hospital and St Bartholomew's Hospital services on the Royal London Hospital site
- Combine the Oldchurch Hospital with Colchester General Hospital in a new unit in Essex

South-east

- Replace separate services in Guy's Hospital, King's College Hospital and St Thomas's Hospital with single unit at Guy's Hospital serving 1.25 million people
- Disruption of Guy's Hospital services during redevelopment may justify retention of King's College Hospital until 1995/96

South

- The Royal Marsden Hospital, Fulham Road to be transferred to the Royal Marsden Hospital, Sutton
- St George's Hospital and the Royal Marsden Hospital to merge

Current position

North-west

Hammersmith Hospitals Trust Strategic Direction confirms specialty rationalisation between two sites. Main radiotherapy base at Charing Cross Hospital and clinical haematology at Hammersmith Hospital. Mount Vernon Hospital position still undecided. No discussion is ongoing concerning centralising the Royal Marsden Hospital at Sutton, or merging the Royal Marsden Hospital with St George's Hospital.

North-central

Likely current sites are University College Hospitals London Trust and Royal Free (Boyle, 1996)

East

Cancer services still predominantly at St Bartholomew's Hospital. **Relocation to the new Whitechapel site expected following completion of site in 2002, subject to PFI.** Discussions concerning Oldchurch Hospital and Colchester Hospital still ongoing, decisions expected later in 1997.

South-east

St Thomas's Hospital will be developed as the major cancer centre, with new units due to be completed by 2002. *King's College Hospital radiotherapy closed. Maidstone has an increased workload taking on more patients who previously came to London.*

South

The position in the south is unclear. No discussion is ongoing concerning centralising the Royal Marsden Hospital at Sutton, or merging the Royal Marsden Hospital with St George's Hospital.

Neurosciences Review

The neurosciences review under the chairmanship of Mr Rab Hide advocated the rationalisation of ten neurosciences centres in London onto five sites.

Specific recommendations

North-west

- Retain service at Charing Cross Hospital; *or*
- build new service on Hammersmith Hospital site

North-central

- Create a joint Royal Free/National Hospital trust with services centralised at a rationalised Queen Square site
- Retain a link to Great Ormond Street Hospital for paediatric services

East

- Centralise Oldchurch Hospital, Royal London Hospital and St Bartholomew's Hospital services on the Royal London Hospital site

South-east

- Transfer services at the Brook Hospital to Guy's Hospital immediately and close the Brook Hospital
- Centralise Guy's/Maudsley services at Guy's Hospital

South

- Maintain current services at Atkinson Morley's Hospital for three years. At end of period consider transfer to Guildford

Current position

North-west

Service has remained at Charing Cross Hospital with support of local health authority

North-central

National Hospital for Neurology and Neurosciences has merged with University College Hospitals London Trust rather than the Royal Free Hospital. Services have remained at Queen's Square. Clinical links with the Royal Free Hospital have been maintained and will be developed.

East

Transfer of services from St Bartholomew's Hospital to the new Royal London Hospital at Whitechapel agreed, subject to PFI. Full business case expected Summer 1997. <u>Position regarding Oldchurch Hospital undecided</u>.

South-east

Decision April 1995 to establish a new neurosciences centre at King's College Hospital incorporating services from the Brook Hospital and Maudsley Hospital. Neurosurgery now at King's College Hospital following transfer of services from the Maudsley Hospital and closure of the Brook Hospital. Proposals for transfer of neurology from Maudsley Hospital to King's College Hospital under consideration.

South

Purchaser review supported by health authority and community health council suggests transfer from Atkinson Morley's Hospital to St George's Hospital, with the replacement unit due in November 2002.

Renal Services Review

The renal review group under the chairmanship of Professor Netar Mallick advocated five tertiary centres in London, one in association with each of the teaching hospital groups, and five specialist centres balanced across the whole of the Thames regions not providing transplantation.

Specific recommendations

North-west

- Hammersmith Hospital, with a link to Charing Cross Hospital, should be the tertiary centre in north west London
- Maintenance haemodialysis should be maintained at the dialysis unit of St Mary's Hospital

North-central

- University College Hospital/Middlesex Hospital should provide tertiary services for the north-central sector
- Transplantation services for older children provided at the Royal Free Hospital in liaison with Great Ormond Street Hospital should be relocated to University College Hospital/ Middlesex Hospital

East

- The tertiary centre should be sited at the Royal London Hospital
- There should, however, be no relocation of either staff or facilities from St Bartholomew's Hospital until adequate facilities are developed at the Royal London Hospital

South-east

- The tertiary centre should be sited at the Guy's and St Thomas's Hospital Trust with the decision regarding which of the two sites used being made by the trust itself
- King's College Hospital should not become a sub-regional centre

South

- The small unit at St George's Hospital should be expanded to become the tertiary centre for the south sector

- Although siting the centre at St Helier Hospital should be rejected because of the potential for academic isolation, the excellence of the service should be retained and enhanced and the need to utilise the skills at St Helier Hospital by the transfer of staff should be addressed

Current position

North-west

Hammersmith's Hospitals Trust Strategic Direction suggests that the major dialysis centre will be located at Charing Cross Hospital but a review is currently under way. Nephrology and transplant services are also provided by St Mary's Hospital but the future of this is still under review.

North-central

The Royal Free Hospital, not University College Hospital /Middlesex Hospital, has been developed as a major transplant centre

East

Renal services will be located on the new Royal London Hospital Whitechapel site, due for completion by 2002, subject to PFI.

South-east

Transplants have been transferred from King's College Hospital to St Thomas's Hospital except for combined liver and renal transplants. Renal unit is likely to stay at Guy's Hospital, at least for the time being.

South

Renal transplantation has been established at St George's Hospital, although a service continues at St Helier Hospital. Commissioning intentions indicate that the St Helier Hospital service should move by 1998.

Plastics and Burns Review

The plastics and burns review group under the chairmanship of Mr Philip Sykes recommended the development of a 'hub-and-spoke' model of services. As part of this the group advocated the rationalisation of the existing 11 centres to just six. the group made no recommendations regarding plastics services at Great Ormond Street Hospital for Sick Children or the Royal Marsden.

Specific recommendations

North-west

- The plastics and burns services at Charing Cross Hospital and Mount Vernon Hospitals should continue so long as associated specialist services remain on site
- The burns unit at Mount Vernon Hospital should remain associated with department of plastic surgery

North-central

- Plastic surgery and burns services at the Royal Free Hospital should be developed
- Plastic surgery and burns services and clinical staff at University College Hospital/ Middlesex should be transferred to the Royal Free Hospital
- Links between the professorial plastic surgery unit at University College Hospitals London Trust and UCL should be maintained with some supporting clinical facilities

East

- Plastic surgery and burns services at the Royal London Hospital should be developed with the transfer of clinical staff from St Bartholomew's Hospital and some consultant sessions from St Andrew's Hospital, Billericay
- Services should be transferred from St Bartholomew's Hospital, although there may be some scope for day surgery to continue, staffed by consultants based at the Royal London Hospital

South-east

- Plastic surgery and burns services should be developed at Guy's and St Thomas's Hospital Trust with inpatient services transferred from King's College Hospital
- Outpatient and day surgery services should continue at King's College Hospital, staffed by consultants based at Guy's and St Thomas's Hospital Trust

South

- Plastic surgery and burns services at St George's Hospital should be developed with the transfer of clinical staff from Queen Mary's Hospital, Roehampton
- Services at Queen Mary's Hospital, Roehampton, should be transferred to St George's Hospital and possibly the Royal Surrey County Hospital in Guildford. A residual outpatient and day surgery facility could remain, staffed by consultants based at St George's Hospital

Current position

North-west

The position is still undecided. Hammersmith Hospitals Trust continues to deliver this specialty from Charing Cross Hospital.

North-central

The University College Hospitals London Trust outline business case suggests that plastics will continue to be developed as a specialist service at University College Hospitals London Trust and will not transfer to the Royal Free Hospital, subject to PFI.

East

All plastics services are currently located at Royal London Hospital Whitechapel.

South-east

In-patient services are to be concentrated at St Thomas's Hospital. Transfer of services from King's College Hospital has been implemented as recommended by review group. Refurbished facilities at St Thomas's Hospital are due to completed by 2002.

South

No changes have been proposed to the existing pattern of services at Queen Mary's Hospital, Roehampton. A local acute services review is currently under way; as a result of this it is possible that the future of the unit at Queen Mary's Hospital, Roehampton will once again come under scrutiny.

Children's Services Review

The review of children's services under the chairmanship of Sir David Hull, took the view that a centre providing specialist services should also provide a full range of child health services to its local population. Within this constraint it was felt that there should be two or three providers of specialist paediatric cardiac service and of paediatric neurosciences and two each of paediatric oncology, nephrology and plastics.

Specific recommendations

North-west

- The Hammersmith Hospital should not continue to provide general inpatient services for children as the volume is too small to support a full range of child health services
- The service for children with muscular disorder should be transferred from the Hammersmith Hospital to Great Ormond Street Hospital
- The rheumatology service which is due to be transferred from Northwick Park Hospital should be transferred to with Great Ormond Street Hospital, Chelsea and Westminster Hospital or St Mary's Hospital
- The Hammersmith Hospital should approach the Institute of Child Health to facilitate their access to sick children for research purposes
- Chelsea and Westminster Hospital and St Mary's Hospital have a wide range of services and the opportunity to develop tertiary services and shared care arrangements

North-central

- Great Ormond Street Hospital should provide secondary level service to its local population in conjunction with other local units
- University College Hospital/Middlesex and the Royal Free Hospital should concentrate on the provision of services for adolescents and adults with Great Ormond Street Hospital admitting all children below a certain age requiring secondary care services
- University College Hospital/Middlesex should link its paediatric services to Great Ormond Street Hospital and concentrate on providing a quality outpatient and day case centre either without inpatient responsibilities or with the level required to support only the A&E
- The Royal Free Hospital should link its paediatric services to Great Ormond Street Hospital and concentrate on providing a quality out-patient and community services either without inpatient responsibilities or with the level required to support only the A&E
- the Royal Free Hospital should provide tertiary adolescent facilities depending on which tertiary services are places there

East

- No tertiary services should be placed on any site until a full range of services for children is established to meet the high level of need in the local population
- Queen Elizabeth Hospital for Children should be moved to the Royal London Hospital site to create a unit with a full range of child health services at secondary care level
- The tertiary services at St Bartholomew's Hospital should be transferred elsewhere in due course, the preferred options being – retinoblastoma to Great Ormond Street Hospital, paediatric oncology either to Guy's and St Thomas's Hospital Trust or St George's Hospital to link up with the Royal Marsden
- Requirements of the local population in relation to outreach outpatient and day care services at both secondary and tertiary level to be reviewed to determine requirements for services at the Homerton Hospital, the current Queen Elizabeth Hospital for Children site and the St Bartholomew's Hospital site
- The Queen Elizabeth Hospital for Children/Royal London Hospital should establish an ambulatory paediatric service and cover arrangements for the maternity and neonatal services at the Homerton Hospital

South-east

- the review group preferred King's College Hospital as a potential site for tertiary services since it had a sensitive approach to the care of the child within a full range of child health services, but noted that it had not been favoured by the adult reviews
- Paediatric neurosciences should be established at Guy's and St Thomas's Hospital Trust

- Guy's and St Thomas's Hospital Trust should be considered as one of the options for the relocation of the paediatric oncology service currently provided at St Bartholomew's Hospital
- Paediatric nephrology services should remain at Guy's and St Thomas's Hospital Trust
- A local review of child health service should be undertaken

South

- The links between St George's Hospital and the Royal Marsden Hospital should be strengthened with St George's Hospital taking management responsibility for the Sutton site. Child health services should be within one clinical directorate
- As soon as a neurosciences centre for children is established at Guy's and St Thomas's Hospital Trust, children should cease to be admitted to Atkinson Morley's Hospital. In the meantime the paediatric input to the service for children here should be strengthened
- The review of acute services set up as a result of *Making London Better* should consider whether the local population is best served by so many separate paediatric inpatient centres

Current position

North-west

The position in the north-west sector is still unclear. Local health authorities and Imperial College are in the process of developing a strategic approach to determine the future configuration of paediatric services across West London. No end point for the development of these services has been set.

North-central

Great Ormond Street Hospital should continue and develop as a major tertiary centre providing a full range of specialist services. Further development of the Great Ormond Street Hospital site is envisaged by the trust.

East

Organisation to transfer Queen Elizabeth Hospital for Children to the Royal London Hospital began 1 April 1995. Paediatric facilities are to be developed at the Homerton Hospital.

South-east

Guy's and St Thomas's Hospital Trust plan to develop a new Women's and Children's Hospital at St Thomas's Hospital incorporating the Evelina Children's Hospital which would transfer from Guy's Hospital. New facilities on St Thomas's Hospital site due to be completed by 2002.

South

Likely to stay on St George's Hospital (Boyle, 1996)

Sources

Specific recommendations

Reports of the independent review groups executive summaries, July 1993
Boyle, S. (1996) Post-Tomlinson developments in London: a description of changes in hospital services in the capital. *Journal of Health and Place* 2 (1): 51–58.
Farrell, C. *Conflict and change: specialist care in London*. King's Fund, October 1993

Current position

Except where stated, these are taken from a written reply to a question in the House of Lords in April 1997.

Glossary and abbreviations

Acheson report	Refers to *Primary health care in inner London: report of a study group commissioned by the London Health Planning Consortium* (1981). This group, chaired by Sir Donald Acheson, identified problems with the quality of primary care in London.
Acute	Describing a disease of rapid onset and often brief duration.
Advocacy	Representation of the interests of an impaired individual by a professional or volunteer as if they were their own.
Agenda 21	An agreement by world governments at the Earth Summit in Rio de Janeiro in 1992 to identify action required to achieve sustainable development in the 21st century.
Borough	Refers to 32 of the 33 statutory local government authorities of London. The other is the City of London (see City of London).
Care of the elderly	The clinical specialty concerned with the treatment of older people. The more dated term 'geriatric medicine' has generally been replaced with 'care of the elderly'.
Care programme approach	Guidelines issued by the Department of Health in 1990 'to provide a network of care in the community' designed to minimise the risk that people with severe mental illness could lose contact with services.
Child health surveillance	Regular examination and monitoring of the health of children below the age of 5 years.
Child protection registers	Records of children known to have suffered from neglect, physical, sexual and emotional abuse or perceived to be at risk from these abuses.
Chronic	Describing a disease of long duration involving slow changes. Often of gradual onset, e.g. arthritis or osteoporosis.
CHS	*see* community health services.
City of London	The historic City of London.
CMHT	*see* community mental health team.
Community health services	Community health services refer to community-based services such as district nurses or health visitors. The term is often applied to an NHS trust providing these services.
Community mental health team	A multi-disciplinary team providing services for people with mental health problems in community settings.
Community psychiatric nurses	Psychiatric nurses working in the community.
CPN	*see* community psychiatric nurses.
Culyer Task Force	A task force headed by Professor Anthony Culyer which investigated the future funding of research and development in the NHS.

Day cases	Elective admissions to hospital where there is no overnight stay.
DGH	*see* district general hospital.
DHA	*see* district health authority.
District general hospital	Hospitals providing a wide range of acute services mainly to a local population.
District health authority	The major purchaser of health services for a local population. Before 1991 district health authorities had responsibility for the management of hospitals.
District nurses	Nurses providing treatment and advice in the community.
DoH	Department of Health.
Domiciliary care	Care given in the home. This often refers to social care such as home helps or meals-on-wheels.
DSS	Department of Social Services.
East London	East London and the City, Redbridge and Waltham Forest and Barking and Havering District Health Authorities (see Appendix 4 for a more detailed explanation).
Elective	Refers to hospital care given after a planned admission.
Emergency	Refers to hospital care given after an unplanned admission.
Family health services	Includes general medical services, general dental services, pharmaceutical services and ophthalmic services.
Family Health Services Authority	The planning and funding body for family health services which succeeded Family Practitioner Committees. In 1996 these were merged into district health authorities.
Family Practitioner Committee	Responsible for family health services before 1990.
FCE	*see* finished consultant episode.
FHS	*see* family health services.
FHSA	*see* family health service authority.
Finished consultant episode	The standard measure of hospital activity in the NHS. The FCE refers to a stay in hospital under an individual consultant. Any given hospital stay may have more than one FCE.
Flowers report	Refers to *London Medical Education – A new framework* (1980). This report recommended that the 34 undergraduate and postgraduate schools of medicine and dentistry in London be grouped together to form six schools of medicine and dentistry.
FPC	*see* Family Practitioner Committee.
General Household Survey	A long-standing government national social survey.
General medical services	Services provided by general medical practitioners.
General practice fundholders	GP practices which hold budgets to directly purchase some services for their patients.
Geriatric medicine	*see* care of the elderly.
GHS	*see* General Household Survey.
GLC	*see* Greater London Council.
GMS	*see* general medical services
GPFH	*see* general practice fundholders.
Greater London Council	The governing body for London which was abolished in 1986. The geographical area covers the 32 London boroughs and the City of London.

HCHS	*see* hospital and community health services.
Health visitors	Community-based health workers providing professional advice and support services.
HEFCE	*see* Higher Education Funding Council for England.
Her Majesty's Stationery Office	Publisher of government publications. Recently renamed the Stationery Office.
High-status London	Barking and Havering, Barnet, Bexley and Greenwich, Bromley, Croydon, Hillingdon, and Kingston and Richmond District Health Authorities (see Appendix 4 for more detailed explanation).
Higher Education Funding Council for England	Official body with the responsibility for funding individual universities and colleges
HMSO	*see* Her Majesty's Stationery Office.
Holistic	In the context of health care, approaches that consider the whole person rather than just the disease.
Home-support services	Social services such as home help and home care.
Hospital and community health services	Refers to services provided by hospital and other NHS trusts, as distinct from family health services.
Hospital-at-home	Schemes for delivering health care in the patient's home.
Hospitalisation rate	Unless otherwise stated, the number of FCEs per 1,000 resident population.
Hub-and-spoke model	A model of specialist service provision (usually referring to specialist hospital care) where a specialist centre, or 'hub', is supported by 'spokes', acute hospitals that refer their more complex cases to the specialist centre.
Immunisation targets	Department of Health targets for GPs for the immunisation of children.
Inner-deprived London	Kensington, Chelsea and Westminster, Camden and Islington, Lambeth, Southwark and Lewisham and East London and the City District Health Authorities (see Appendix 4 for more detailed explanation).
Intermediate care	There are many definitions of intermediate care. The following themes are typical in any definition: services are supportive; care follows a nursing rather than medical model; care is delivered near or in the patient's home.
Junior doctors' 'New Deal'	Government scheme, introduced in the 1990s, to reduce junior doctors' hours.
Length of stay	The duration in days of a finished consultant episode.
LIG	*see* London Implementation Group.
LIZ	*see* London Initiative Zone.
LMC	*see* Local Medical Committee.
Locality purchasing	Groups of general practices in an area collaborating in order to make purchasing recommendations for a range of secondary care.
London	In this report, London refers to the area of what was the Greater London Council.
London Health Care 2010	Final report of the first King's Fund Commission on London.
London Implementation Group	The body created to oversee the changes to London's health services outlined in *Making London Better*.

London Initiative Zone	The areas of London where special funds were made available for investment in primary care. These were the following district health authorities: Ealing, Hammersmith and Hounslow, part of Brent and Harrow, Kensington Chelsea and Westminster, Camden and Islington, East London and the City, part of Enfield and Haringey, part of Redbridge and Waltham Forest, part of Barking and Havering, part of Bexley and Greenwich, Lambeth, Southwark and Lewisham, part of Merton, Sutton and Wandsworth and part of Croydon.
LOS	*see* length of stay.
Making London Better	The Government's response to the Tomlinson report, which was the basis of recent changes to health service provision in London.
Medical training grades	Hospital doctors below the level of consultant.
Mental Health Reference Group	A group established by the London Implementation Group to consider mental health services in London.
Mental Health Task Force	A body commissioned by the Government in February 1994 to look at services provided for people with severe mental illness in London.
Mental illness specific grant	Specific grants for the development of social care services for people with mental health problems, established in 1990.
Mid-year population estimate	An estimate of the population of an area produced by the ONS. It is based on the estimated resident population at the previous Census adjusted for births, deaths and migration.
Minimally-invasive techniques	Surgical techniques which involve comparatively little incision. Often referred to as key-hole surgery.
Minimum standards for GP premises	Standards for GP practice premises set out in the rent and rates scheme. These relate to issues such as disabled access and adequate waiting areas.
Mixed-status London	Merton, Sutton and Wandsworth, Brent and Harrow, Ealing, Hammersmith and Hounslow, Enfield and Haringey and Redbridge and Waltham Forest District Health Authorities (see Appendix 4 for more detailed explanation).
NHS and Community Care Act 1990	The act which implemented the 1991 'NHS reforms', instituting the purchaser/provider split and the internal market.
NHS R&D	*see* NHS Research and Development.
NHS Research and Development	Department of Health directorate responsible for research and development in the NHS.
NHS trusts	'Self-governing' hospitals or groups of hospitals created by the NHS and Community Care Act 1990.
North-central London	Camden and Islington, Barnet and Enfield and Haringey District Health Authorities (see Appendix 4 for more detailed explanation).
North-west London	Brent and Harrow, Ealing, Hammersmith and Hounslow, Kensington, Chelsea and Westminster, Hillingdon District Health Authorities (see Appendix 4 for more detailed explanation).

Nursing home	An institutional dwelling either owned and managed by a local government authority, a voluntary agency, a legally registered company or an independent proprietor and registered with a local authority, or owned and managed by an NHS trust. Nursing homes are required to register with the local health authority under Part 2 of the Registered Homes Act 1984. Those managed by NHS trusts are subject to internal NHS 'registration and inspection'. To be distinguished from residential homes although some establishments provide both levels of care.
Office for National Statistics	Formed in April 1996 through the merger of OPCS and the Central Statistical Office.
Office of Population Censuses and Surveys	The official body responsible for the collation and analysis of Census data. It was replaced by ONS in April 1996.
ONS	*see* Office for National Statistics.
OPCS	*see* Office of Population Censuses and Surveys.
Patient's Charter	The NHS section of the Citizen's Charter which confirmed the public right to services and outlined standards pertaining to time spent on waiting lists, waiting time in accident and emergency and outpatient departments, cancelled operations and day case rates.
PFI	*see* Private Finance Initiative.
Pharmaceutical services	Community-based services for the provision of drugs. Part of family health services.
Practice nurses	Nurses working in GP practices.
Primary Care Act 1997	The National Health Service (Primary Care) Act 1997
Primary Care Support Force	Replaced the Primary Health Care Forum on the demise of the London Implementation Group in 1995.
Primary Health Care Forum	Established by the London Implementation Group to develop an agenda to improve primary care in London.
Private Finance Initiative	Scheme introduced by the Conservative Government in the 1990s to encourage private-sector investment in public-sector capital projects.
PS	*see* pharmaceutical services.
Psychogeriatrics	The clinical specialty dealing with mental health problems among older people. Also known as 'old age psychiatry'.
Purchaser efficiency index	An official index designed to provide a single overall measure of efficiency trends for district health authorities.
Reed report	Refers to *Review of health and social services for mentally disordered offenders and others requiring similar services* (1991).
Regional health authority	Prior to April 1996, an intermediate tier of management between district health authorities and the Department of Health.
Regional office	From April 1996 the successor to the regional health authority.
Residential home	An institutional dwelling registered with a local authority social services department to provide residential care for older people or others. May be owned and managed by a local government authority, a voluntary agency, a legally-registered company or an independent proprietor. Residential homes are registered with the local authority under the Residential Homes Act 1984. To be distinguished from nursing homes although some establishments provide both levels of care.

RHA	*see* regional health authority.
RO	*see* regional office.
Screening targets	Department of Health targets for GPs for screening patients for cervical cytology.
Section 117 procedures	Procedures relating to the discharge of mental health patients into the community.
SHA	*see* Special Health Authority.
SMR	*see* standardised mortality ratio.
Social services department	That part of a local government authority responsible for providing or ensuring the provision of personal social services for local residents.
South London	Merton, Sutton and Wandsworth, Kingston and Richmond and Croydon District Health Authorities (see Appendix 4 for more detailed explanation).
South-east London	Lambeth, Southwark and Lewisham, Bexley and Greenwich and Bromley District Health Authorities (see Appendix 4 for more detailed explanation).
Special Health Authority	Hospitals in London linked to the postgraduate institutes.
SSD	*see* social services department.
Standardised mortality ratio	An age-standardised method of comparing a schedule of death rates with a reference schedule, often the national schedule.
Supervision register	Register that mental health service providers are required to hold of all people with severe mental illness who may be a significant risk to themselves or others.
Supported housing	Small-scale housing developments with additional services for a particular client group, often people with mental health problems or learning disabilities.
Tertiary services	Very specialised services available only at a limited number of hospitals.
Todd report	Refers to *Report of the Royal Commission on Medical Education* (1968). Recommended closer links between the University of London and medical schools.
Tomlinson report	Refers to *Report of the Inquiry into London's Health Service, Medical Education and Research* (1992).
Total purchasing	Experimental scheme by which GP fundholders purchase emergency as well as elective care for their patients.
Transitional relief	Temporary extra funding to London NHS trusts and health authorities.
TULIP team	An intensive community outreach and support scheme for people with mental health problems in Haringey.

References

Acheson, D. (1981) *Primary health care in inner London: Report of a study group commissioned by the London Health Planning Consortium*. London: HMSO.

Audit Commission (1986) *Making a reality of community care*. London: HMSO.

Audit Commission (1994) *Finding a Place. A review of mental health services for adults*. London: HMSO.

Banta, D. (1990) *Emerging and Future Health Care Technology and the Future of the Hospital*. Cardiff: Welsh Planning Forum.

Benzeval, M., Judge, K. and Solomon, M. (1992) *The Health Status of Londoners: A comparative perspective*. London: King's Fund.

Benzeval, M., Judge, K. and Whitehead, M. (eds) (1995) *Tackling Inequalities in Health: An agenda for action*. London: King's Fund.

Boyle, S. (1996) Post-Tomlinson developments in London: a description of changes in hospital services in the capital. *Journal of Health and Place* 2 (1): 51–58.

Boyle, S. and Smaje, C. (1992) *Acute Health Services in London: An analysis*. London: King's Fund.

Boyle, S. and Smaje, C. (1993) *Primary Health Care in London: Quantifying the challenge*. London: King's Fund.

Boyle, S. and Hamblin, R. (1997) *The Health Economy of London*. London: King's Fund.

Challis, L. and Pearson, J. (1996) *Towards an analysis of the health and social care needs of older Londoners*. London: King's Fund.

Coote, A. and Hunter D. (1996) *New Agenda for Health*. London: IPPR.

Deans of the Medical Schools of the University of London (1997) *The contribution of London's academic medicine to healthcare and the economy*. London: University of London.

Department of Health (1990) *The Care Programme Approach for People with a Mental Illness referred to Specialist Psychiatric Services. Joint Health/Social Services Circular HC(90)23/LASSL(90)11*. London: HMSO.

Department of Health (1993a) *Making London Better*. London: HMSO.

Department of Health (1993b) *Department of Health Press Release H93/908*. London: Department of Health.

Department of Health (1994) *Supporting research and development in the NHS: A report to the Minister of Health*. London: HMSO.

Department of Health (1995) *A policy framework for commissioning cancer services: A report by the Expert Advisory Group on Cancer to the Chief Medical Officers in England and Wales: guidance for purchasers and providers of cancer services*. London: Department of Health.

Department of Health (1997) *The patient's charter: mental health services*. London: Department of Health.

Department of Health and Home Office (1991) *Review of Health and Social Services for Mentally Disordered Offenders and Others Requiring Similar Services ('The Reed Report')*. *The Reports of the Service Advisory Groups, and Overview*. London: Department of Health.

Farrell, C. (1993) *Conflict and Change: Specialist care in London*. London: King's Fund.

Fulop, N. and Hensher, M. (1997) *A Survey of Needs Assessment Activities in London Health Authorities*. London: King's Fund.

Government Statistical Service, Government Office for London and the London Research Centre (1996) *Focus on London 97*. London: The Stationery Office.

Ham, C., Smith, J. and Temple J. (1997) *Hubs, spokes and policy cycles: An analysis of the policy implications for the NHS of changes to medical staffing*. London: King's Fund.

Harrison, A. (1997) *The London Health Care System*. London: King's Fund.

Harrison A., Dixon J., New B. and Judge K. (1997) Can the NHS cope in future? *British Medical Journal* 11 January 1997 314: 139–142.

Health Advisory Service (1997) *Services for people who are elderly*. London: The Stationery Office.

Inner London Health Authorities (1995) *Hospital services for Londoners: A report by the Inner London Health Authority chief executives*. London: Inner London Health Authorities.

Jarman, B. (1994) *The Crisis in London Medicine; how many hospital beds does the Capital need?* London: University of London.

Johnson, S., Ramsay, R., Thornicroft, G. *et al.* (eds) (1997) *London's Mental Health*. London: King's Fund.

Joseph Rowntree Foundation (1995) *Inquiry into Income and Wealth*. York: Joseph Rowntree Foundation.

King's Fund (1992) *London Health Care 2010: Changing the future of services in the capital*. London: King's Fund.

London Research Centre (1996) *The Capital Divided*. London: London Research Centre.

London Implementation Group (1993a) *Report of an independent review of specialist services in London: Cancer*. London: HMSO.

London Implementation Group (1993b) *Report of an independent review of specialist services in London: Cardiac*. London: HMSO.

London Implementation Group (1993c) *Report of an independent review of specialist services in London: Children*. London: HMSO.

London Implementation Group (1993d) *Report of an independent review of specialist services in London: Neurosciences*. London: HMSO.

London Implementation Group (1993e) *Report of an independent review of specialist services in London: Plastics and Burns*. London: HMSO.

London Implementation Group (1993f) *Report of an independent review of specialist services in London: Renal*. London: HMSO.

London Health Partnership (1997) *London Health Partnership: Some lessons*. Unpublished paper.

Mays, N., Morley, V., Boyle, S., Newman, P. and Towell, D. (1997) *Evaluating Primary Care Development*. London: King's Fund.

Mays, N. and Dixon, J. (1996) *Purchaser Plurality in the UK*. London: King's Fund.

Meara, R. (1992) *London's Legacy: Aspects of the NHS estate in London*. London: King's Fund.

Meara, R. (1997) *A Capital Conundrum: The effect of the Private Finance Initiative on strategic change in London's health care*. London: King's Fund.

MHA (1997) *A Survey of Acute Hospital Configurations in London*. London: King's Fund.

Millar, B. (1997a) Nine to five. *Health Service Journal* 9 January 1997 107 (5534): 12–13.

Millar, B. (1997b) Falling between the cracks. *Health Service Journal* 27 March 1997 107 (5546): 13.

Morley, V, Holland P. and Scott R. (1997) *Primary Care in London*. London: King's Fund.

NHS Executive (1994a) *Introduction of supervision registers for mentally ill people* (HSG(94)5). London: HMSO.

NHS Executive (1994b) *Guidance on the discharge of mentally disordered people and their continuing care in the community* (HSG(94)27). London: HMSO.

NHS Executive (1996) *24-hour nursed care for people with severe and enduring mental illness*. Leeds: NHS Executive.

Nichols, R. (1997) *Seismic Shift or Noisy Tremor? A personal perspective of the changes and processes of change in London, post Tomlinson*. (forthcoming) London: King's Fund.

Office for National Statistics (1996) *Regional Trends 31*. London: HMSO.

Oxford and Anglia Regional Office (1997) *Assessing the impact of Calman*. Unpublished paper.

Peck, E., Smith, H., Barker, I. and Henderson, G. (1997) The obstacles to and opportunities for the development of mental health services in London: the perceptions of managers. In: *London's Mental Health*, Johnson, S., Ramsey, R., Thornicroft, G. *et al.* (eds). London: King's Fund.

Ritchie, J. H., Dick, D. and Lingham, R. (1994) *The Report of the Inquiry into the Care and Treatment of Christopher Clunis*. London: HMSO.

Rivett, G. (1986) *The development of the London Hospital System 1823–1982*. London: King's Fund.

Secretary of State for Health (1989) *Working for Patients*. London: HMSO.

Secretary of State for Health (1997) *Developing Partnerships in Mental Health*. London: HMSO.

Steiner, A. (1997) *Intermediate Care: A conceptual framework and review of the literature*. London: King's Fund.

Stocking, B. (1992) *Medical Advances and the Future Shape of Acute Services*. London: King's Fund.

Tomlinson, B. (1992) *Report of the Inquiry into London's health services, medical education and research*. London: HMSO.

Towell, D., Best, G. and Pashley, S. (1997) *London Health Care: Rethinking Development*. London: King's Fund.

University of York (1997) *The Relationship Between Hospital Volume and Quality of Health Outcomes*. York: University of York.

Warnes, A. M. (1997) *The Health and Care of Older Londoners*. London: King's Fund.